PRAIRIE LIVES

Between the Lines

PRAIRIE LIVES

The Changing Face of Farming

TEXT AND PHOTOGRAPHS BY LOIS L. ROSS

Canadian Cataloguing in Publication Data

Ross, Lois L.
    Prairie lives: the changing face of farming
Bibliography: p.
ISBN 0-919946-48-8 (bound)   0-919946-49-6 (pbk.)

1. Farm life — Prairie Provinces. 2. Agriculture — Economic
aspects — Prairie Provinces. 3. Farms — Prairie Provinces.
4. Women in agriculture — Prairie Provinces. I. Title.
HD1790.P7R67 1985   630'.9712   C85-098519-6

Published by Between The Lines

229 College Street
Toronto, Ontario
M5T 1R4

Printed in Canada

Between The Lines is a joint project of Dumont Press Graphix,
Kitchener, and the Development Education Centre, Toronto. It receives
financial assistance from the Canada Council and Ontario Arts Council.

ACKNOWLEDGEMENTS

Although an author may hide out to write a manuscript, books are not written in isolation. To bring an idea to publication a lot of people give a lot of time in the form of discussion, feedback, and support. There's no way to measure the worth of contributions, so I'd like to thank all equally: Connie Kaldor, Dario Argento, Camille Bell, Brent Bennett, Jill Bennett-Seldon, Charles Reasons, Sandy Hunter, Terry Pugh, Glenda Brown, Judy Genaske, Linda Duncan, John Kolkman, Irene Dickie, Heather Nord.

As well, my family deserves a special thanks for providing an idyllic space to hang my hat, along with favours and advice during this book's germination and growth.

In addition, to those people who agreed to be interviewed and photographed, your openness, prairie hospitality, and free meals will always be remembered.

Finally, thanks to my editor, Robert Clarke, and to the Between the Lines collective for being sensitive towards rural issues.

Without the confidence and trust of all involved, this book would remain unwritten.

L.L.R., Gravelbourg, Saskatchewan,
December 1984

For Ernie, Cécile, Cy, and René

TABLE OF CONTENTS

1   **ACKNOWLEDGEMENTS**

4   **PREFACE**

6   **INTRODUCTION**

13   **CHAPTER ONE** Small Farmers: A Prairie Culture in Peril

39   **CHAPTER TWO** Farm Women: The Unrecognized Resource

57   **CHAPTER THREE** Farm Bankruptcies: Going, Going, Gone

67   **CHAPTER FOUR** Farming: The Natural or Chemical Way?

83   **CHAPTER FIVE** Organic Pioneers: Proof in the Pudding

111   **CHAPTER SIX** Co-operative Farming: The Mavericks

135   **CHAPTER SEVEN** Corporate Farming: Bigger and Better?

155   **CHAPTER EIGHT** Prairie Farmworkers: Immigrants and Hired Hands

168   **GLOSSARY** Notes for City Slickers

170   **BIBLIOGRAPHY**

Preface

As I drove down prairie roads to complete this work I had hours to think about the differences between the urban and the rural. Those differences became very tangible at times. It had been years since I had last been able to experience them, and sometimes they showed up in small ways.

Late one evening I parked my car and trailer on an approach off a backroad in rural Saskatchewan. Stepping out of the car I noticed the entire northern hemisphere lit up by thousands of stars. The sensation startled me as I gazed and tried to define the outline of constellations I had learned about years before in school. I could only recall two. In past cultures and societies it was a daily ritual for people to observe, study, and name the stars. These days we forget about the stars, their beauty and necessity, because massive electrical lights block them from our vision. Besides, short of being lost in the wild, we no longer need stars to tell the weather or direction.

Most of us forget about agriculture for much the same reason. Advances in technology mean that it takes fewer and fewer people to grow our food. At one time four out of every five Canadians lived on the farm. Now, one person out of twenty-five does. Most urban people do not keep gardens and would rather seed lawns to hide the dirt. Supermarket shelves are always stocked and a food crisis seems an irrational, crazed thought. So, we forget.

Often, when forced to think about food issues we grapple for words and make statements that have no basis in fact. As one farmer explained: "It doesn't take people very long to lose touch with the actual 'out there' problems."

One farm woman told me that she thought many Canadians had become "foreigners to the land."

As an illustration of this, I've heard well-educated people who are generally up to date on current issues argue that we needn't worry about agriculture "because most farmers are rich anyways." Still others have voiced satisfaction and amazement about the technological advances within agriculture. For them technology is a force that has liberated people from getting their hands "dirty" growing food. They accept fewer farms as something progressive and do not question the applications of technology — the fact that technology can be used for good or bad — or the ramifications of a dwindling rural population, or even the fact that some people like, want, and need to get their hands "dirty." They look on farming as an occupation that people are trying to escape from, or as work that people do when they haven't had the opportunity or education to choose something different.

I suppose it is this type of simplistic and unfounded argument, heard repeatedly over the years, that more than anything else prompted me to embark on this project. The goal of the book is to provide a clearer understanding of what farmers think about food production and the direction of agriculture. While numerous other works have been written on the same topic, this documentary effort is an attempt to both see and hear from those people who are central, those people who are the protagonists in the food production system. Who should know better the actual "out there" problems?

The interviews were usually recorded around a kitchen table, sometimes in places of obvious prosperity, sometimes in glaring poverty. The accompanying photographs will, I hope, make tangible these people, their culture, hopes, and problems. The format I have chosen is an attempt to create on paper a reality that is lived daily in fields and farmhouses.

The people interviewed were chosen at random with an eye towards representing different types of farms, farmers, and regions. I took to the road for four months and wandered from farmstead to farmstead asking residents' views about everything from commodity prices, food quality, soil quality, farm size, to the environment. While the documentation of these prairie people could have continued endlessly, I feel that this book is representative of the diversity and eclecticism, the triumphs and failures, of prairie agrarians. I purposely excluded Hutterite colonies and Native farmers, sensing that the practices, history, and current influences on both these groups are too far removed from the mainstream to be dealt with adequately in this book.

While I included a number of interviews with women, the majority have been with male farmers. The male-dominated farm continues to be a fact of life and few women farm alone. Women are of course an integral part of farm life, but many are still trying to overcome the economic and mental barriers that have placed them in a second-class position. Many farm women preferred to step aside and let their husbands speak. Many are still wrestling with their identity and are only beginning to realize that they too are prairie farmers.

Finally, why a book singling out western Canadian farmers? While there are farmers in all parts of Canada and their work is equally valuable — and they share many common difficulties — a documentary work on prairie farmers as a single group was necessary not only because of similarities in history and region, but also because many of the problems being faced by western Canadian farmers are specific. The prairies are the major export-producing area and also the focus of the dramatic changes taking place in agriculture. The west is the final frontier, the last bastion, the site of a forthcoming wave of concentration in land ownership and a resultant desecration of a population. In eastern Canada farm consolidation peaked in the 1960s as record numbers of farmers went bankrupt or left the farm. During the 1980s and 1990s the prairies will be the region to suffer most from the unprecedented impact of fewer and larger farms.

As a member of the fourth generation of a prairie agrarian people, I am not an outsider to the problems. My roots are in western Canadian agriculture and rural people are my culture. I feel lucky to have been granted a past that allowed me to be equipped to undertake this task. I can identify with the joy, sweat, tears, worry and wrinkles etched on many young faces. My role as a journalist and documentalist is not so much to separate myself from the task at hand in the name of "pseudo-objectivity," but rather to understand, emphathize , and substantiate the story. If I were a "foreigner," this effort would have suffered.

This photo-documentary is my way of dealing with the destructive, mounting tide that is overtaking prairie agriculture. It's my way of asking you to listen to the story of a people who are being displaced. Many of the faces in this book will not be around the farm in another decade. These farmers are testimony that what is happening to prairie agriculture is regressive rather than progressive. Rather than stepping forward we are jeopardizing a culture, a system of food production, and the environment.

This book is not intended as a nostalgia trip. It's an attempt to gaze into the future so that all of us, farmers, business people, and consumers, can better decide what kind of world we want to live in. In that sense, perhaps, it is also a call to action.

As farmers and consumers we have rights, but we also have responsibilities. While none of us can rewrite history, we have the responsibility not to repeat it continually until it is too late.

L.L.R.

Introduction

By the mid-1980s, the family farmers I talked to had managed to survive a tense decade of dramatic increases in farm operating costs and inadequate increases in commodity prices. The last four years had been the worst. Farmers' existence today seems to be inceasingly tenuous and few of them count on things getting better. A decade ago most of them still believed that the medium-sized family farm was here to stay. Today most of them say that agriculture is changing quickly and that the family farm as we have known it is rapidly becoming a part of prairie history. Some farmers even believe that there is a concerted move to push them off the land.

Still, the goal on all the farms I visited was to try in the face of overwhelming odds to keep it together. As one farmer said, and many echoed throughout the course of numerous conversations, "It's just a matter of sooner or later and we hope that for us it will be later."

The toughest thing to ask farmers is to speculate on how long they will last. One young farmer who started out a few short years ago expected that in 20 years he would likely be looking for another place to live and work. By then the farm would be gone and he would be in his mid-forties. That view, however, may be overly optimistic. Others have sat at the kitchen table, taken a deep breath, and admitted openly that it could be as soon as tomorrow. But even in the most negative of circumstances I encountered few farmers who were prepared to let the farm go, although it would have made much more economic sense to sell out, move on, save the sweat and stress, and rearrange the pieces of a life sooner rather than later.

Every prairie farmstead is different. All farmers talk about different aspects of their operations. One of them tells me how he is building productive soil by allowing cows to roam on a sub-marginal patch and thereby fertilize it. In a few years he hopes the patch will grow forage crops. Another points to the industrial development that is taking away prime agricultural land. He can't let that happen without putting up a fight. Then there's the farmer who sees nothing wrong with massive amounts of chemicals, large farms, and fewer farmers. He hopes to be one of the survivors.

Farmers talk about the home quarter and the number of generations it has been in the family. They recall the small shack, now the henhouse, that they were born in or that their mother was isolated in during her bout with tuberculosis decades ago. They point to the mailbox with a stem made from the plough their grandfather first used when he came to this land. Farmers talk in generations, not in years or decades. On most family farms there are the vestiges of past lives, hardships, and aspirations. They take the shape of out-of-use machinery, wind-blown buildings, or simply a collection of old truck licenses nailed to a fence. All of these markers seem to state: "We're here to stay."

While farmers cling to memories, they also cling to hope. The days when the weather was the major problem on the family farm are over. Sure, the weather still makes or breaks a number of farmers, but so do a lot of other factors. These days the optimism and spirit that characterize farming are still evident, but a number of other issues come into play — issues that are putting the squeeze on almost all farmers.

The overwhelming problem is that most farmers are now living on less, paying more for everything, and borrowing more than ever before in an effort to stay afloat. In 1969 the average net farm income on the prairies was $4,000. In 1983, it was $13,000. And while that appears to be an increase in real dollars, prairie farmers are earning less now than they were in 1971. Alberta producers, for example, have taken at least a 36 per cent drop in income.

The reason for declining incomes is rising farm costs combined with low commodity prices. Overall expenses have increased almost 200 per cent since 1971. Prairie land prices alone increased 400 per cent between 1971 and 1981. Among the eight major implement companies, machinery prices have increased on the average by 13 per cent annually, with tractors and combines increasing by at least 18 per cent. Since 1971 the average capital value of a farm has risen seven times.

Collectively, Canadian farmers have accumulated more than five times the farm debt owed in 1972, with prairie farmers owing half of it. The Farm Credit Corporation released a survey in the fall of 1984 showing that 16 per cent of prairie farmers — about 25,000 — are in "severe financial stress" and are carrying 74 per cent of the total debt-load. On average these farmers owe $215,000 dollars each. Translated, that means they own only a little more than half of their farm operations.

Prairie farm net income has not kept up to the rise in operating costs for a multitude of reasons. The major one is that grain prices are tied to a monopolized international market. That market is controlled by a handful of grain companies — of which Cargill is perhaps the best known — estimated to control 80 or 90 per cent of global grain sales. The needs of prairie farmers are not foremost in this market. They consider the prices they get for grain to be too low to meet costs. While a system of stabilization programs has been put in place by both levels of government to ensure that producers do not carry the entire burden of low prices, these plans are linked to international prices by relying on a domestic price determined on a five-year average. Farmers say they are being "stabilized in poverty." One farmer put it simply: "If there was no one to fleece there wouldn't be millionaires."

Since most Canadian grain is grown for export, international prices have a huge impact. While grain-producing nations jockey for position in tariff and trade agreements, and at various times have held talks in the hope of forming alliances to improve international grain prices, the reality is that countries are competing amongst themselves for a share in the market. Consequently, grain prices set on the international open market reflect external supply and demand factors rather than internal costs of production.

The result is that in 1983 a bushel of wheat destined for export sold for $5.58. In 1984 the price was even lower. Taking into account the increase in overall costs, a bushel of wheat should sell for well over $10. No one is quite sure what the break-even point is for farmers — or for that matter, the breaking point.

All farmers talk about economics, meaning the increasing costs of production alongside commodity prices that consistently refuse to follow suit. But some farmers also go beyond pure economics to analyze and discuss the ramifications of using a totally money-based approach to agriculture. These farmers talk about urban encroachment, the problems of "mining" the soil, producing for the export market, and destroying the environment with chemical inputs. They also talk about the dwindling farm population and the problem of increasing farm size and land concentration.

Often they talk about the "cheap food policy," a phrase used to pinpoint the failure of the marketplace and the government — essentially, the failure of the system — to return enough to average producers to enable them or their children to continue as full-time farmers. For farmers, "cheap food" means the growing or raising of produce as cheaply as possible, either for foreign markets or to provide a cheap source for processors. For farmers, "cheap food" more often than not means that a crop is sold at or below the cost of production.

These farmers say that promoting a wheat economy and "cheap food" means that agriculture in western Canada is underdeveloped rather than diversified and self-sufficient. While farmers are kept busy growing for export, tariffs on imported foods are kept low. This also drives down the price of local produce, a problem that has long

Irma Fleming,
Millet, Alberta

plagued the beef industry.

Still, 25 per cent of the annual grain crop is used domestically, and some Canadian farmers have called for a distinctly separate pricing system in the hopes that a higher domestic price for wheat would help offset losses in times of low international prices, and better reflect production costs. But the federal government's response has been less than adequate. While the domestic price of wheat can differ from that of export under the Canadian Two Price Wheat Act, the legislation states that a bushel cannot be bought or sold for less than $5 or for more than $7 within Canada. The prices are obviously not related to costs of production.

One of the reasons these parameters have been set is that urban consumer groups, manufacturers, and processors claim that a rise beyond export prices in the domestic price of grain will produce rises in food prices. A recent example occurred in late 1984 when the Canadian Wheat Board, faced with a very bad crop year, announced it would raise the domestic price of wheat about $1 a bushel over export price. The Grocery Manufacturers of Canada, which represents the baking industry, was quick to complain that the higher price could cost consumers $150 million in 1985. The association, in a typical response, said its industry would be forced to import flour-based products from the United States, with possible ramifications for 6,000 workers.

But the minister responsible for the Canadian Wheat Board, Charles Mayer, responded that wheat is such a small factor in the actual retail cost of bread that prices would rise by less than one cent per loaf. He even went a step further, noting that in Winnipeg, for example, bread prices rose 48 per cent between 1980 and 1984 while wheat prices had remained the same.

The federal government's strategy is to increase exports and tag domestic prices to international ones for the sake of expedience, yet try to stabilize consumer prices for Canada's urban workers, thereby avoiding civil strife. As one farmer explained it: "We are raping the rural to subsidize the urban." The point is to allow wholesalers and retailers a profit without upsetting consumers too much. The farmer is largely ignored. After all, at 4 per cent of the population, the farm vote does not count for much. Meanwhile, in 1983, as Saskatchewan farmers' net income declined by 24 per cent over the previous year, Loblaw's accumulated close to $53 million in profit — a net income increase of 16 per cent. Dominion Stores charted a 15 per cent increase and Safeway 13 per cent during the same period.

Farmers are not sacred. There are good, bad, and indifferent farmers, the same as any other people in any other community or occupation. But the work farmers do, as many will tell you, is basic and of primary importance. As one farmer told me: "We supply the energy that is the most important in this society. We supply the energy that runs the human body."

As I wandered through the three prairie provinces, the eclecticism, diversity, and, all too often, contradictions among farmers sprang forward. Some farmers are the archetypal "rugged individualists" who believe that the law of supply and demand coupled with less government and an "unbridled" open market are the only ways to go. These farmers are self-proclaimed free-enterprisers and while they may bemoan the loss of farms, their individual actions encourage the trends. These are the farmers who believe that "bigger is better" and that progress means expansion. They have adopted a strict growth mentality and take pride in the notion that they are self-made people. But as one small farmer explained: "If you're fighting to survive you'll accept protection, but if you get over the hump, like the big guys, and have her made you figure you don't need it."

Other producers see clearly that the old economic laws of supply and demand are the source of the problem. These farmers say that the only solution is an agricultural policy that has its priorities not simply in production but also in the preservation of a strong rural population, in the environment, the soil, food self-sufficiency, diversity, and a fair return on commodity sales. These farmers want more controls, but the kind of controls that provide a genuine path for their participation.

These two types of farmers, the entrepreneur and the interdependent, environmentally concerned farmer, represent the differences between agribusiness and agriculture. Agribusiness refers to a corporate-controlled agriculture and, as authors Roger Burbach and Patricia Flynn put it in their book *Agribusiness in America*, "an integrated food system that extends from farm to factory to consumer — from food production to the manufacture of farm implements and pesticides to food processing and food marketing." It is an industrial form of farming where success is based on specialization and expansion, with profit the main concern. The strategy is short-term and fast-paced.

Agriculture, on the other hand, has traditionally placed emphasis on a sense of rural community and the things that sustain a community or culture. The emphasis, rather than being primarily on the dollar sign, is placed on such factors as a strong population base, meaning many farmers, co-operation among neighbours and within the community, and protection of the environment and the soil through diversity. This means, of course, protection of a whole livelihood for the future generations who will make up the community and farm the land.

These days the farming community is becoming increasingly polarized between agribusiness and agriculture. The dollar is segregating prairie farmers and in many cases is pitting neighbour against neighbour and sibling against sibling. While the majority of farms are still family operations, there are increasing numbers of farmers who, because of economic pressures, are adopting the agribusiness mentality.

The increasing polarization between agriculture and agribusiness raises another important question in the farm community. As more and more farmers leave the land or are forced into bankruptcy, the term "viable farmer" is used as a euphemism to disguise an economic problem. What is a viable farmer? In the strict "government document" sense, a viable farmer is one who is able to make optimum returns per total investment and where everything else is secondary. The viable farmer, then, becomes the person best able to juggle falling commodity prices, rising equipment costs, and escalating land values, all by continuously increasing crop volume and production. At some point, however, the environment and the culture must be sacrificed to balance the economic scale. That point has been reached in prairie agriculture and the term "mining the soil" is used to refer to the juncture.

Following this, the non-viable farmer becomes the one who may not want more land, or who decides that using chemicals for the sake of increased volume is not a solution, or who tires out and quits, realizing that he or she is a farmer and not a high financier. To say the least, the term "viable farmer" is confusing and misleading.

Despite the pressures, most farmers are willing to risk a lot, sometimes everything, to remain on the land. The reasons that farmers cling to the soil have much more to do with culture than with economics. Even when the economics of the occupation no longer make complete sense, farmers continue to stroke the land. Most can't imagine another lifestyle. The thought of moving to an urban area provokes a pained gaze. A lot of farmers I spoke with asked rhetorically: "Who are we working for?" In the next breath the conversation twists towards the farmer who recently sold out, or the number of spring auction sales in the district. The farmers' enduring sense of community and culture is immensely apparent in the sad, often bitter tones of such conversations.

My dictionary defines culture as the tillage of the soil, quantity of bacteria produced, or a particular form or stage of intellectual development or civilization. In the past, agriculture has combined all of these. And even now agriculture is cohesive. It revolves around a community and a lifestyle and the generations that have allowed their work to shape their thoughts, ideals, and future.

Today's farmers are still deeply tied to a culture, but the pressures they cope with no longer allow them to feel that they are working for the future, for food production, or even

for society. Although many loathe the situation, they know and feel they are working for the dollar. What's worse is that most of them say they have little choice but to fall in line with the standard if they want to continue farming. Many make compromises that erode their integrity and pride.

Farmers also know that while things are tough on the land, the grass is not greener anywhere else. As one farmer said: "Difficult as farming is, where else is there to go? When it comes down to it we are not badly situated." Farmers at least have the feeling that they can provide food for their family, if nothing else.

The point is that while there are still farmers who believe in agriculture, prairie agrarian life is changing rapidly. The problems inherent in the transition to agribusiness are wide-ranging and far-reaching. The solutions are more difficult to pinpoint but perhaps by understanding the problems through the eyes of farmers we'll be better prepared to discuss new futures and directions.

This book includes all types of farmers. It includes the diversity and the contradictions of agrarian prairie communities. But I think it's important to understand that while some farmers are party to the change, farmers themselves have not mapped out the direction. All of them are reacting, morally or immorally, rightly or wrongly, to the demands imposed upon them by ad hoc government policies and agricultural experts working largely to protect the interests of the secondary agri-food industry — the food processors, manufacturers, and distributors. At the same time as Canada's cheap food policy makes it difficult for farmers to gain a full-time living on the farm, that same policy is providing the agri-food industry with an inexpensive — and profitable — source of food for processing and distribution on the domestic or export markets.

The same forces and factors currently shaping prairie agriculture and moving it towards agrarian concentration have already moulded the economics of many Third World nations — remember the banana republic — and are now at work within most industrialized nations. That is to say that at all levels, even the most important primary level, food production is being concentrated into the hands of fewer and fewer individuals or corporations. Because of economic concentration both farmers and consumers, whether they realize it or not, are neighbours with much in common.

Both face the ramifications of a highly concentrated food production system. Fewer companies distribute food on the retail level and fewer farms produce it. In Canada, 86 per cent of all retail food sales are funnelled through five wholesale companies controlled by major food outlets. Consumer associations have stated their alarm over the concentration. As these purchasing groups increase their buying power, those independent food processors that do exist find their bargaining power declining as wholesalers increase their imports of food through foreign-owned sub- sidiaries. To ensure profit levels, wholesalers need a cheap source of raw foodstuff and so squeeze the primary pro- ducer, the farmer. That in turn forces concentration at the primary level as farmers jockey to increase crop volume and make up for low prices.

Over 60 per cent of fruit and vegetable canning, flour and breakfast cereal sales, and over a third of all food and beverage shipments are controlled by foreign-owned plants. This country imports 57 per cent of its vegetables. These vegetables, which can be grown in Canada, cost consum- ers more per pound than those grown locally. No doubt a portion of imports is to allow for the "convenience" of eat- ing out-of-season produce. While the shorter growing sea- son definitely influences the types of vegetables grown on the prairies, there are still few farmers growing even those vegetables best suited to western climates and soils. In 1981 in Saskatchewan, for instance, there were only 90 vegeta- ble growers who cultivated a total of no more than 3,000 acres — less than five sections of land.

Neither consumers nor the family farmer benefit from concentration of distribution. In fact, concentration leads to low commodity prices for the farmer, who is faced with the choice of mining the soil to increase volume, growing one crop (a monoculture) to save labour and expenses,

working off the farm to supplement income, expanding to balance the economic scale, or if all else fails, selling out or going bankrupt.

Concentration of both farmland and ownership of the agri-food sector offers no guarantee that consumers will perpetually be provided with a relatively cheap source of food. In fact it only promises to see us paying more as competition dwindles and the power to determine the price concentrates along with the land and industry.

So far, Canadian consumers pay out about 18 per cent of their total income towards food. Among consumers, those with the lowest salaries, those who can least afford it, pay the highest percentage of income for food. Among farmers, the smallest — those who do not have the volume to soften the blow of low commodity prices — suffer the most. The key point to remember is that farmers do not de- termine the price of their commodities any more than con- sumers have the ability to increase their salaries automati- cally when the cost of living rises.

Wendell Berry, author of *The Unsettling of America*, suc- cinctly defined the nature of the "farm problem" in an ar- ticle written for *The New York Times*:

> The most important question is whether or not good
> farming can be understood as an industry. The an-
> swer is that it cannot be so understood. The reasons
> are complicated but they may be summed up in two
> facts: first, farming depends upon living creatures
> and biological processes, whereas the materials of in-
> dustry are not alive and the processes are mechanical;
> and, second, a factory is, and is expected to be, tempo-
> rary, whereas a farm, if well farmed, will last forever —
> and, if poorly farmed, will be destroyed forever.

If the industrialization of agriculture and the move fur- ther into agribusiness continue, as promised, both family farmers and consumers will be the victims. And, once again, those who can least afford it will pay the most.

A Prairie Culture in Peril

Wendell Mullet finds it interesting that I've decided to take to the road and ask farmers what they think about it all. He's slightly startled about what would motivate me to ask his view on food production, when as a consumer all I have to do is head to the grocery store and pick up what I need. He puts down the bale he's dragging to the barn for his milk cow and stops to talk:

"You know, for most people food is so convenient that they don't stop to think about what's happening. Often we forget that there's a crisis going on. We try to ignore it and sometimes take a ho-hum attitude towards it. Even farmers become numb to disaster if it's repeated often enough. But, the point is, these problems aren't going to disappear."

The decline in family farms in Canada is not new. What is new, though, is the fact that many farmers feel the decline is dangerously accelerating. In 1961 there were over 600,000 farmers in Canada; some 200,000 of these were on the prairies. Two decades later the numbers have fallen to just 318,000 in Canada and 154,816 on the prairies. Canada has lost half of its farmers, the majority of them gone from eastern Canada during the 1960s. During the last 15 years this country has lost an average of 21 farmers a day, with 7 a day disappearing in the prairie provinces.

While it is sometimes argued that this loss is due to sheer happenstance or to individual mismanagement, the federal government predicted and encouraged the trend years ago. In 1969 it released a controversial report, *Canadian Agriculture in the Seventies*. The report essentially stated that because of a then surplus of agricultural pro-

duction and the fact that a third of farmers were living below the poverty line, it would be wise to eliminate the problem by axing two-thirds of the Canadian farm population by 1990. It was the federal government's method of "waging war on poverty." In 1969, 9 per cent of the Canadian population lived on the farm. By 1981 only 4 per cent remained. On the prairies, farm numbers dropped from 21 per cent of the populace to 11 per cent during the same time frame. The federal government's mission to deliver farmers from the land was nearly accomplished.

In keeping with that goal, other government documents have estimated that by the year 2000 there will be fewer than 100,000 major producing farms in Canada, operating large tracts of land as partnerships and corporations. Half of them will be on the prairies. In 1981 a federal report on agri-food strategy, *Challenge for Growth*, supported the trend by outlining the need for fewer, more specialized, and capital-intensive farms.

But in *Challenge for Growth*, rather than using rural poverty and overproduction as the guise for farm depopulation, the government changed its tune somewhat, instead citing the need to increase production to meet potential export demands. Those exports would come largely from prairie production. The government acknowledged that agriculture meant billions of dollars to the economy and that each dollar's worth of exports caused another $5 to ripple through the economy. According to the report, large, efficient farm operations were the only way to meet the increasing need for food in an ever hungry world. By the year 2000, it estimated, Canada could increase the food sector's output by two-thirds and cash in on expanded markets. Interestingly, that need would come largely from the Third World nations, who have traditionally not had the money to buy imports for their populations.

What the 1969 and 1981 reports proposed, in effect, was the elimination of the weak in order that the strong might flourish and expand. The government's assumption that many small producers are not "viable" is a false one, as evidenced by the conversations with farmers in this book.

But in late 1984, when the Farm Credit Corporation released a survey outlining the extent, impact, and reasons behind the financial problems on the farm, a controversial ripple spread through the agricultural industry. The FCC survey shows that the 17 per cent of Canadian farmers and 16 per cent of prairie producers in financial trouble are also the most productive. Those farmers least likely to survive are, on a dollar for dollar basis, twice as productive as the 76 per cent of Canadian farmers in a high-equity and stable position. But these same farmers, the majority of them young, are forced to use borrowed money to provide themselves with a net income.

To put it bluntly: if production is the gauge, the farmers going out of business today are some of the most "viable" in the country. No wonder so many farmers on the following pages keep mentioning that "something's wrong."

Given the federal government's agricultural strategy and hunger for export dollars, along with the current bankruptcy rates and the average rate of attrition for farmers during the last 15 years, prairie farm producers within the next decade may well be facing a decline in numbers that will rival any similar period in their history. The next farm exodus is due to take place on the prairies, the area that accounts for almost 75 per cent of agricultural exports. The agri-food strategy is primarily based on those exports of grain.

The *Challenge for Growth* report stated clearly that the major impediment to increasing exports was the Crow's Nest Pass Freight Rate Agreement, which essentially froze grain freight-charges to producers. The fight to retain the Crow lasted a decade and divided the farm community. The rate is now history and producers face annual increases, increases that must come from their net income and cannot be passed on through commodity pricing. Academics and statisticians are now working hard to assess the number of farmers who will give up due to adverse economic factors, including the loss of the Crow. Speculation on the exact impact is at best imprecise, but the trend is clear.

Small farmers are also at the mercy of provincial governments and the vagaries of voting. In 1973, for instance, an innovative concept was legislated into existence in Saskatchewan under the provincial New Democratic Party. The Saskatchewan Land Bank Commission was to allow for farmland to be transferred from one generation to another under a long-term lease, with annual rental paid on a percentage of production. It thus dealt with one of the biggest headaches for family farmers: the survival and economic viability of the farm in the long term. The Land Bank also included the option to buy the leased land, but few farmers during the nine-year history of the program chose that path. In 1982, however, the Land Bank was abolished by the new Progressive Conservative government, under the peculiar charge that it was "robbing people of their heritage."

The Conservative government replaced the Land Bank program with an 8 per cent interest-on-loans program. "I don't think that will help young people who don't have any land, to get started," Saskatchewan farmer Ron Horvath told me. The maximum loan under the program was to be $350,000. "That amount of money would only buy you four or five quarters, on which you'd never make enough to pay for the interest on the land — let alone the machinery you are going to need," Ron Horvath said. It is clear that as farmers move off the land, fewer and fewer will be able to balance the statistics by starting up.

Farm leaders estimate that because of declining income and the inability of producers to pass on freight increases through the price of their products, anywhere from 20 to 40 per cent of prairie farmers will quietly, and in some case vociferously, leave the farm. Depending on the scenario, 12 to 23 farmers could be lost on the prairies during the next ten years. That's one out of every two or three existing farms. By 1990 or slightly beyond, the number of full-time farmers could closely correspond to what the federal government predicted in 1969.

While there have always been small farmers — and likely always will be because some rural people have the stamina to sacrifice even the basics to live on the land —

16

the trends clearly indicate that fewer and fewer operators
will produce for the market. But trends are based on current conditions. If the conditions change, if the priorities
are reassessed, it is possible to reverse the trends. The
question that we must ask ourselves — and that many farmers are asking — is what happens to the land, the environment, rural communities, and the food production system
in general when things like imports and exports and meeting the national balance of payments become more important than food self-sufficiency, agricultural diversity, and
a way of life.

Wendell and Jonathan Mullet,
Bluesky, Alberta

RON HORVATH   The clutch of Ron Horvath's blue half-ton truck squeaks on depression and thumps on release, as if keeping pace with the conversation and the farmer's baritone voice. Ron is talking about the dynamics of farming with two brothers and a father. He says it works well, but his father still carries a major load on the farm — it's hard for him to let go after all of these years of farming.

The "boys" definitely treasure having "dad" around, but they don't like to see him working this hard. With the Saskatchewan Land Bank Commission dismantled, the Crow rate gone, and the farm economy in disarray, it's hard to convince a parent to let go. Ron Horvath was the 1983 President of the Land Bank Tenant's Association, which represents about 400 of the 2,700 lessees in the province.

Ron, his father George, and brothers Marvin and Gordon farm five sections and keep 200 head of cattle on the edge of Leross, Sask. There's one thing about farming, notes Ron. If you can manage to hang on to the land "you'll never starve."

RON: When the Land Bank was formed there were very few young farmers in our area. There wasn't any money in farming. Quotas were low, a lot of people out of school left the farm to get a job or went to a technical college or university. They weren't going to stay on the farm — you couldn't make enough money to go out on weekends. The Land Bank gave some of these people the opportunity to come back into farming without tying their parents up with another mortgage that they'd have to spend another 25 years paying for. That's one of the reasons I went into it — I didn't have to tie my father up.

If you look back and study the philosophy behind the Land Bank, it was that the land should never be sold — that it could be farmed under a long-term lease that lasted until a farmer retired. Then he could roll it over to some of his heirs. They could continue to farm it for the rest of their lives.

The idea behind that, and I think there is wisdom in it, is that for years and years family farmers have been buying a piece of land, working all their lives to pay for it. Then, when they finally get it paid for, they have to run around and sell it so they have some retirement money because everything they made in farming had to be put back into the land. If they sold it to their children, their kids would spend their lives paying for it. The government said, how many times should people have to buy this land over and over? How many generations are going to be burdened with the purchase of land?

Then the Crow Rate issue just throws a different light on farming as a whole. Now we're going to have to pay more and more every year. And we know one thing — at the present time there isn't a lot of money in farming. The profit margin is so low right now that we don't feel we can afford any extra whether it is through freight rates or rental on our leases. It might be the straw to break the camel's back for a lot of us. And if you project down the road, if we pay five or eight times the Crow Rate, that means there won't be too many smaller farmers who will be able to continue. I'd say that on a farm that is grossing fifty thousand dollars, your actual net income would be no more than seven or eight thousand a year. And that would be for a family.

Most of the young farmers are hanging on. If something drastic happens, like if mother nature was to frown on us and give us one or two bad years, a few crop failures, well, there are a lot of farmers working on operating loans and they're just hoping they can pay those off so they can continue to borrow on it. It's not a good situation.

It really makes me wonder how much longer the family farm is going to be around. I think the only reason a lot of farms are hanging on is because the spouse is doing a lot of work at virtually no income and the children do a lot of work when they're old enough to drive a tractor — again at virtually no income. If the net income is cut further by way of lower prices or increased operating costs there'll come a point where you'll say this way of life isn't worth it anymore. If we can't afford to live in a decent house or drive a decent vehicle, then maybe farming isn't worth it — the way of life isn't worth it. If the family farm goes then I think the only route for farming in Canada will be through corporate farms.

Maybe there will be some co-operative farms.

It makes me sad to think that the way of life may be gone. We've never had much money but the lifestyle is good. When we were kids we always had the back-40 to run around on, we could go and hunt a magpie or a crow. I think the fun was having that freedom, that open space. I would like to think that small farmers still have a long time to go, but looking at it realistically, there could be a big change in less than ten years.

Gordon, Ron, and Marvin Horvath,
Leross, Saskatchewan

FRANK STEVENSON created the Mountain Springs Ranch in the Peace Country of Alberta in 1946, as a homesteader. Most of the land on the seven quarters he owns and the nine he rents had to be "brushed and broke."

"I tell everybody who homesteads not to expect anything for ten years," says Frank, a tall, sturdy, opinionated man. "But it's healthy, hard work and at the end of the day you feel like you've accomplished something."

Frank gives me a grand tour of his farm and its surroundings. He introduces me to high and low wild berries and to soap holes, which, depending on their diameter, can clutch and sink a boot or a tractor. He shows me his hand-picked rockpile — one of three piles gathered from eight acres. Frank runs 80 head of cattle as well as growing grain, and supports the idea of a national meat authority that would set prices according to costs of production and take the guesswork out of raising beef.

FRANK: Before farming went the way it has you seemed to have more time to pick berries. And I enjoyed it. That was part of the way of living. You went and you picked wild berries. You took two or three days off to do that sort of thing. It was a break. Now it seems like you have to make every hour count. If you pick berries you feel like you're wasting time.

The country has got a cheap food policy. When you should be getting your cost of production, you're selling at a loss. The consumer is getting meat way under cost and it's to the farmers' detriment that they're getting it that way. There's no way that a young farmer can borrow money for land and machinery and grow food as cheaply as we are growing it and still make the payments. Even with my land being paid for I know how hard it is to make ends meet.

So, when feed grain prices are low the only way out is to feed the grain to your livestock. But if everybody starts to do that we'll have over-production. I'm against the open market on feed grains for that reason. I feel that the Wheat Board has done a good job, but they have to have control over all of the grain to do a better job for us. Because our feed grains are on the open market and not controlled by the Wheat

Board, the price has dropped.

When you are dealing with the law of supply and demand alone, it's tough. When the cattle get scarce and the prices for beef go up, then I should be raising cattle, right? But I can see that I'm not going to make a dollar on them if I wait because everybody else will be bringing theirs to market at the same time and the bottom is going to drop out of them. The only safe way to do it is on the principle that a bird in the hand is worth two in the bush. So, you sell your cattle early, you dump them on the market, and start over again. It upsets the whole operation because then you have extra feed on hand. We shouldn't have to be doing it that way. We shouldn't be forced to play the markets and gamble. The prices should be more stable. We should have a fairly good idea of what we're going to get for that animal once it's finished. But you have no idea.

Two of my sons are farming with me, but I didn't encourage it. It's sure helped me out in terms of work. But I'm subsidizing them by quite a bit because if I eventually sold the farm that money would provide my pension. But I can see that, if they're going to get established, I'm going to have to donate what I've built up. It shouldn't be that way. It doesn't make me mad because I hope I'm healthy enough to hang on for awhile. But, if a person had to retire, it might be different.

On the other hand, when they were all away from home, I started to think... What did I build this up for? Why did I bust my butt opening up this land if the kids don't care about farming? Oil money was glittering in their eyes and they were pulling out. Now, the way they're working on the farm, if things were working right they'd be able to buy me out without any problem. But it isn't that way because of the economics.

If they're bull-headed they may last awhile. But it takes only a few crop losses and you're out of business. The margin has narrowed right down to nothing. A few years back you didn't have those big payments to make and if you lost a crop all you had to worry about was keeping grub on the table. And if you were lucky enough to get a moose and you had a good garden and a few head of cattle or pigs to sell to buy the necessities, you could get by. But now your cattle are pretty well booked to cover your expenses.

It seems to be getting a little harder every year and it shouldn't be. It should be easing off, but it isn't.

Frank Stevenson,
DeBolt, Alberta

BEN AND GRACE BUNIAK farm 701 acres in northern Saskatchewan near Rosthern. They have a mixed farm and have operated since 1974 on land homesteaded by Ben's grandfather in 1911. The Buniaks have two tractors — a 105-horsepower and a 60-horsepower — and have invested an estimated $120,000 in farm equipment, all of which classifies them as small prairie farmers.

The rabbits kept in a shed on the farm are a constant reminder of a deal gone bad: an estimated 50 rabbit producers were forced to absorb losses when a meat distributor in the southern part of the province went bankrupt. Yet, despite the costliness of this failed attempt at rabbit farming, both Buniaks coddle the expensive balls of fluff with no hint of sourness. They can even joke a bit about how much each one is worth in sweat and tears. But behind all the joking, and sweat and tears, is the fact that the Buniaks derive no income from their farm and have to subsidize their land with off-farm income.

BEN: It's really frustrating when you go to the bank and they look at your assets and say: "Well, you're worth 250,000 dollars." I don't have 5,000 dollars for a down payment on a tractor, let alone being able to afford the necessities. We are half-finished remodelling our house and we can't afford to finish it off.

GRACE: We made more money with our cattle the first two years we were here than we have in the last six. We were encouraged by Farmstart and the federal government's agricultural representative to get into cattle. We did, and a year or so later the price just dropped. We paid 500 to 600 dollars for each cow and a year and a half later they were at 150 or 200 dollars tops.

That's one of the reasons we went into the rabbit business. It looked like something good to get into. We had a ten-year contract, borrowed 8,000 dollars to buy the does and equipment and then, just as the rabbits were ready for market, the company we were dealing with went bankrupt. We had 900 rabbits. Now we can't recoup our money on them and nobody wants to buy the equipment. We mortgaged a quarter of land for the loan. The bank enticed us with a lower interest rate if we mortgaged the land.

BEN: I had to go out and get a job this year. Our net income is a minus figure. We are basically living on family allowance cheques of 86 dollars a month. Then Grace makes perogies which brings in anywhere from 200 to 500 dollars a month. That's at one dollar a dozen. It pays the bills. We're thankful we can do it.

We knew we wouldn't be rich people when we moved out here. That was not our intention. We just wanted a good family life. We haven't had a holiday in 16 years. We never leave the farm.

We don't want to make farming sound all negative. It does put a smile on your face at times. One time, it was seven in the morning and it had just rained. Our daughter, Vanessa, was outside. The birds were singing and she said: "Isn't it beautiful out here, dad!"

We take a certain amount of pride in this farm. We are the third generation on this land. We have a plaque to commemorate the family farm. Maybe it doesn't mean that much to certain people, but it means a lot to us. We'd like to keep the farm. We won't give it up without a struggle. We'll fight to keep it.

Ben and Grace Buniak,
Rosthern, Saskatchewan

24

GEORGE FRIESEN has farmed for 25 years near Lacombe, Alta. He's a second-generation farmer who crops 1,000 acres and keeps about 50 cows. As a founding member of the Alberta group Preserve Agricultural Land (PAL), George has fought for the retention of agricultural land in the face of industrial encroachment.

After a friendly handshake, George embarks on philosophical discussions about the meaning of farming. In fact, whether he is standing in the farmyard, driving down the road in a half-ton, relaxing in town with a coffee or at home at the kitchen table, his conversation never strays too far from the land base. Finding a label for an innovative, inquisitive, and gentle man like George isn't easy.

GEORGE: My biggest concern now is for the welfare of the soil, not the welfare of the industry. Whereas it used to be my priorities were the other way around. But if you do that and the land disappears, then you don't have an industry anyway.

If we talk about stewardship, which is taking a responsible look at and action concerning the resource we deal with — the land — the general trend, especially in the last 15 or 20 years, has been toward one-enterprise farms, either grain or dairy or hogs or cattle. The trend has been away from mixed farming. The reason is economics. It's less difficult to make management decisions for a monoculture. With one operation it should, economically, on paper, give you a better cash return. But it becomes more difficult to be responsible in your stewardship of the land resource because if you only raise hogs, and buy your feed from the next person who is only raising grain, that means the fellow that is raising hogs is only concerned about the cheapest price he can get the grain for. That determines his bottom-line profit.

The fellow that grows the grain doesn't have natural fertilizer from animals so he has to totally rely on artificial fertilizers to keep his rotation going. Without animals it's no value to him to have a grass rotation, which replenishes the soil with fibre and nitrogen. We're falling short of what we could be doing if we adopted a multi-enterprise operation.

My occupation is farming. It's my way of life. To do anything less than the best I know how is immoral.

There's a combination of things that are steering and changing our culture. We've produced artificial individuals — companies — that have more economic benefits than the real individual. So, one of the things that happens with a monoculture is that people, even farm people, have formed artificial individuals. That artificial individual never dies and has a tendency to grow larger and larger. What's happening now, during a recession, is that the companies that go broke are picked up by larger companies and I'm afraid that eventually, unless we change our ideas about how we want agriculture to be, that more and more the land is going to fall into the hands of artificial individuals.

I'm sure there are large corporations today, such as Purina and Cargill, that would have no qualms about vertically integrating their operations into primary production. So what you get is a complicated scenario of monoculture and at the same time these big industries producing the product on the farm, moving it to the elevator, and then to export. They gain control from start to finish. I don't expect to see this in my lifetime, but it will get a good start. It's already happening.

Corporations don't destroy the land intentionally, but the easiest route is to take a single enterprise, a monoculture, and it grows bigger and bigger. The individual has no other interest than the job and the economics, and when that happens I'm sure that the land becomes just like an oil well. It's there just to be used as long as it will give a return and when it doesn't you discard it. You lose that relationship between the real person and the soil and if you lose that then you're going to destroy the land.

A corporation is simply a name. It doesn't have a conscience. It doesn't know the difference between right and wrong. The existence of that name depends strictly on profitability and if something needs to be done to ensure that profitability and it's not in the best interest of the soil, that name can't tell the difference. And the people who work for that name are not going to say anything either, because their job is on the line.

George Friesen,
Lacombe, Alberta

RICHARD SLYKHUIS   In May 1983 a barn burned down near Kisbey, Sask. It belonged to Richard Slykhuis and it put him in a bind. The insurance provided a substantial sum of $70,000, but this wouldn't pay half the costs to rebuild.

Richard farms a half-section and has a herd of 58 Holsteins. He heard about an empty barn near Arcola, a half-hour drive away. The barn belonged to Richard Arndt, a near-bankrupt farmer, and Slykhuis was milking his cows in it when I talked with him.

RICHARD: I'm going to farm for the rest of my life. I'm hoping to retire in a shack on the corner of the farm and watch the kids work. And if they need something I can jump in the car and go get it for them. I'd like my kids to farm if they choose to, and I think they will because they've been brought up with it. I left my own home in the hills north of Carlyle, but every time I go back there even now, there's these old memories, the hills are still in you. The feelings never get away from you if you're brought up tied in with the land.

I feel uncomfortable about the city. A lot of people there aren't even happy with their jobs. They're there because of the bucks and they have to do something. They're clock watchers. And on a holiday everybody is in a big hurry to get out of the city to go to the lake.

But farming sure has changed a lot. Years ago 40 cows took a lot of time. These days you're working on volume. Because of the machines we got we can do more work. There's less back-breaking work. What it is now is the management of figures and more machine technology. Because you can handle more, you can farm more. As the machines get more expensive you have to buy more land.

People are constantly talking about more production and feeding the world. There are people starving, but in this country and elsewhere the food doesn't get to them because of money. So who's regulating the production? It's the rich.

The large farmers here, some of them are so big they don't figure they need any protection on the market. But in a lot of countries where they don't have marketing boards — like the United States — the farmers are monopolized and the companies rob them of their profits: profits that should be used to better a farmer's life. If I didn't have a milk marketing board right now the market might be flooded with milk and I'd have to be dumping all of my milk. Marketing has to be controlled.

The most important thing is to like what you're doing and enjoy your life. Maybe you're going to be poor, but forget about that damn money and smell that nice air and feel that ground. But by thinking and trying to get bigger and better we're getting away from caring and away from getting back to the earth.

Richard Slykhuis,
Kisbey, Saskatchewan

28

JIM VISSER is a 44-year-old Alberta potato grower. He began growing the vegetable at 19 when he took over the 320-acre farm from his father. Things were a lot different in 1957. For one thing, his residence didn't have a house number. Peddlers did not come to the door every second day, consumer coupon-books did not arrive in the mail, and he did not have to license his dog. Jim says he is no longer a typical vegetable farmer. His land is now part of Edmonton and these days, he says, he feels more like a tenant on a piece of urban land.

In June 1981, the city of Edmonton annexed 86,000 acres of land. Jim's land was part of the package. The year before, to fight the annexation, Jim had helped organize a group called TOPSOIL (To Please Save Our Irreplaceable Land). Now TOPSOIL is fighting for an agricultural preserve within the city, in an attempt to save land from urban sprawl and prevent massive profits from being generated by speculation. The figures speak for themselves. In 1965 an acre was worth about $250. In 1975 it went up to $1,500. Then in 1980, a year before annexation took place, that same acre rose to $17,000. Although the price has since dropped to $6,000 an acre, it is still far beyond its agricultural value. These days falling potato prices are only a small part of Jim's worries.

JIM: Twenty-five years ago there was an active community here. Now most of the people living in this area are working in the city and most of the land is in the hands of speculators. They want farmers to farm it for tax reasons and so there are farmers on it. But these farmers are not doing a very good job because it is not their land anymore. I feel very sad to see some of the land not being farmed properly and productively.

The farmstead isn't being improved and the land isn't being looked on as land that should be improved by rotation practices. Even cultivation practices just to prepare the seed bed and to keep the weeds down aren't done as well as they might be. And I'm sure the farmers would do a better job if they were looking to live here on a permanent basis. Their whole ambition, their focus, is elsewhere. That's what spec-

ulation and looking to get a lot of money for the land has done. The power of money — it's really materialism expressed concretely before our eyes.

If you fall into that rut I believe it affects how you relate to the land and how you relate to life in general — all of your values. You treat the land as a commodity rather than for its created purpose, which is to produce food and fibre to sustain life. You don't treat it with respect as a renewable resource. I think that it affects your motives — right from the heart.

If you speculate on the land I suppose you can use the money to buy land elsewhere and set up the farm of your dreams. But, even that, it seems to me, is not right because you're leaving behind something that is going to be destroyed because of your move. The land will be paved over. Moving into a new area with all that money from speculation artifically throws the land prices out of kilter in that new area, so that the land is no longer priced at an agricultural value.

We have decades of proof that leaving the preservation of agricultural land up to the marketplace does not work. We are losing agricultural land at a very dramatic rate in this province — particularly the better lands, for instance in the Edmonton-Calgary corridor and around Edmonton.

I feel that government's role and its responsibility are to steward agricultural land. They should not allow land to function as a commodity in the real-estate market for speculative purposes. It is a resource just as much as oil and gas, the most valuable public resource we have. The province should be zoned. We know we need cities. We know that we need parkland. We need forestlands and places for the animals to live. And we know that we need foodlands. I'm not saying that any one of these areas is more important than the other, but it's clear that we have options for all of these areas and it's really incumbent on our government to say: "Now this is foodland and it may not be touched for other purposes."

The annexation has had a negative impact on our operation. Now that we are in the city we don't know when development is going to take place. Development has the connotation of being something progressive — improvement and so on. But, this development is really regressive. Farmers in this area are blessed with some really fine land. It has ideal tilth for vegetable production and intensive farming. But we are sitting on this land, not knowing whether we can make capital investments to improve our farms. What's the sense of buying additional equipment, expanding our operations to provide the city with additional fresh produce, if this could be taken away in a decade? Really, what's happening in this area is that farming is on hold or regressing because of the annexation.

We have the right to refuse to sell to the developers. But that does not improve our situation very much because if everybody else sells, and we are surrounded by speculative land, then it makes it difficult to hang in. And if we were to hang in, there is the incompatibility with urban residences right next to your farm. Personally I am committed to not selling. I feel that it is morally wrong to do it. That's how I feel about it today. There are times when I think about selling and I wonder if I'm being a fool, but then I don't want to be part of the problem. I don't want to capitulate.

When you farm a field for a long time and you've improved it you know every little knoll and every little dip. You develop a feeling for it. Just the thought of this land being taken out of food production and actually being paved over hurts. Strong words such as rape go through my mind. It's total destruction. It's clear.

Jim Visser,
Edmonton, Alberta

WENDELL AND JOYCE MULLET homesteaded in the Peace River Region of northern Alberta, near Bluesky, six years ago. Although they both originally came from farm families, for a time they flirted with city life. Wendell worked as a salesman and a carpenter before the Mullets decided to move north. Now they own a quarter of land and rent 16 quarters. In all their farm is 2,700 acres, with 180 acres under cultivation. The rest is in what the Mullets call "the development stage." Eventually, they would like to double their head of 50 cows. Wendell both teaches part time and does carpentry work because the farm does not yet provide an economic return to the family.

WENDELL: I think the "why" of being out here is one of the foremost questions. Originally we came because we weren't satisfied with our urban lives. We were perpetuating a lifestyle we couldn't justify. I was working in construction, building excessively luxurious homes. We see a luxurious lifestyle as closely tied to destruction and keeping others down. Looking at it globally, we couldn't feel comfortable with North American lifestyles and our standard of living.

The challenge came to us to promote human life and survival more than luxury and destruction. I have to admit our attempts to move in that direction have been faltering. It's new ground in a way. We don't have any clear models. We are really going against the grain, we feel.

For example, to give you an idea of our concerns, in Central America multinationals have moved in, in co-operation with totalitarian regimes, and have made a lot of money selling sugar and coffee. The small farmers have been pushed off the land while the multinationals hire cheap labour to export these luxury cash crops to industrialized nations — all the while downgrading the possibility for meaningful existence in these Central American countries.

We'd like to identify with these small farmers in other parts of the world by lowering our expectations and not depending on luxury and consumerism. We want to break the whole cycle.

I've always sensed a tension between the rural and the urban. We are seeing an unhealthy kind of tension. Urban people are removed from food production and they no longer understand it. They like the convenience of the city and tend to romanticize about the countryside. So what you have are urbanites dreaming about the country. It's a schizophrenia. As they romanticize the countryside they continue a lifestyle which degrades the land through urban sprawl, pollution, and environmental carnage. People are getting away from how you provide for life.

The lifestyle of industrial society is posing a serious threat to the environment and agriculture. By being part of a lifestyle that depends on more and more products and conveniences, it poses a threat to the land.

Now the direction of agriculture is towards industrialization...simply looking at maximizing production without concern for the health of the soil itself. We don't agree with it. But, at this point, there is a lot of money to be made selling chemicals and machinery to farmers. As long as people have an interest in that it will not necessarily promote the best use of the land.

On the farm, we feel that we are part of the creative process. We are not trying to be self-sufficient through the exploitation of others.

Wendell and Joyce Mullet,
Bluesky, Alberta

Vic Murray takes me out to the shed on his farm near Young, Sask., to show me the 16 white plywood crows stored in it. Each one of those crows has logged a lot of prairie miles. It must have been odd to observe the statuesque figures secured inside the box of a half-ton truck travelling down a dirt road towards a farm meeting.

Vic won't take sole credit for the White Crow Campaign, but there is little question that he was one of its prime organizers. The White Crows are a piece of history, as well as sculptures that attest to the political art inherent on the prairies.

Vic is a 61-year-old registered seed-grower who farms 2,000 acres. He believes that despite the federal government's removal of the Crow's Nest Pass Freight Rate, the Crow can return. Without it he estimates that 18,000 prairie farmers will go out of business within the next few years and double that within five. In 1984 farmers faced a 55 per cent freight rate increase, meaning that collectively western farmers would pay an estimated $7.2 million more in freight — a cost that must be absorbed by each of them.

Vic: I don't know what importance food has to get to before we'll protect the land. The cost-price squeeze is getting so drastic now that we are forgetting about pollution in order to make a buck. And somewhere down the road we are going to be paying for our mistakes.

Around here a farmer should be able to make a living off a section of land. If we had the right prices for the right products we could do that. But right now it's impossible because of the government strategy. The pressures are immense to work longer, have bigger equipment, buy more land and one thing just eats up the other. We are putting in more acres in a day than we could in a week a few years ago and we're still behind. So we are really not gaining. I've been expanding since I started farming, with the hopes of having land for my family, and I know when I was farming a section and a half by myself I had time off. I could get my crop in and have a little time to myself. After I added more to that portion I seemed to be not gaining anything. There's no

profit margin. And it's affecting the nerves of farmers today. They're uptight. They're pressured.

At one time we were grassing back some land. Now we can't because the sale of hay isn't profitable. We have to go to commercial fertilizers to keep our income up. We have to go for the bushels now. At one time we could wait for the wild-oats to grow, then seed, now we have to get over our land fast. We can't wait, so we have to use spray. So, that's another operation and another piece of equipment.

If the trend continues I think maybe we can forget about the family farm. Families may band together and do the best they can. But when you get a farm as large as mine who's going to buy you out? There's only one group of people that can and that's the corporation or the larger farmers. This has been going on since the first homestead, but now it's accelerating. And one main reason for that is the Crow Rate issue.

The "White Crow" campaign came about this way. I felt real unrest amongst the farmers. And being a Wheat Pool delegate I felt we had to do something about the unrest because we were waiting in limbo for the "Pépin Plan" and nothing was happening.

You get a lot of ideas when you're laying in bed or driving the tractor. I had the white crow idea on a Friday and I mentioned it to the boys at the rink on a Sunday. On Monday morning we had a meeting with 47 members of the Pool committee and we decided to do something. And that was before the "Pépin Plan" came out. We needed something for the media. The discussion was black crows and sign them with white pencils but then you ended up with a white crow. So then we decided we'd go for a white crow and sign it with black pencil.

It really caught on. We got close to 16,000 signatures on 16 big crows and 6 small ones. Then we travelled to Ottawa to present the crows to Parliament. When we were going down people were giving us a dollar to save wildlife. They thought we were out to save a species of bird, but when we were on our way home they knew all about the Crow Rate. Right across Canada they knew what the Crow was. At least we've really made our mark in that respect. When you talk

Vic Murray,
Young, Saskatchewan

Crow in Ottawa they know it's a freight rate, not a bird.

At the presentation in Parliament every crow had the written petition on it, which made it legal. The security let us take them around to the back elevator because they were petitions. Nobody asked any questions. They had no thought that they weren't petitions. A petition is like a cheque, you can write it on wood or paper and it's still a cheque.

The way we were going to present them was to show one little crow, then pull the curtains and show that the other crows were there and that was the end of that. We weren't trying to disturb anything. But, Madame Sauvé, the Speaker of the House of Commons, got a little excited and I don't think she acted correctly. It shocked her a bit and she acted in haste. It was a sensation in Parliament. Never before have they called the guards in. Seems you have to do things a little sensational to get things across. We noticed when the presentation was made that Mr. Pépin had left.

The Crow Rate is just the buttering on the bread, really. The real reason for changing the Crow Rate is that they want to get rid of the Canadian Wheat Board. They want to mo-

nopolize the food industry. There are companies that want to control the food industry, because food is power and they know that. And the more you can control food and the movement of food, the more power you'll have — far more than money can buy.

I think the Crow Rate is just a move for monopolies in this country to take over. All they have to do is get the variation in freight rates and they could control the entire movement of grain in the country. Say Saskatoon ships grain 20 cents cheaper than Young — that will close down Young in a hurry and farmers will haul to Saskatoon. Then once Young is gone they can put the freight rate right back up in Saskatoon. Then farmers will have to pay the extra for that 80 miles of hauling.

What the Crow Rate does is it controls the profit of the railways. If you get rid of the Crow Rate there's no control on their profit and then the farmer will have to put in the extra money. If you end up with only 15 places to deliver in Saskatchewan, well, the farmer will have to have a large truck or hire a truck — maybe he'll quit rather than go to that extra expense.

Getting rid of the Crow Rate is a concerted move towards land concentration. The first thing they want to get rid of is the Crow. The next thing they want to get rid of is the Canadian Wheat Board. And the next thing they want to get rid of is a bunch of these little nuisance towns and farms we have around the place.

And then maybe, when we have these giant farms, we can start a tractor out in the morning and go west until dinnertime and have lunch and then come back home for supper. I'm not being farfetched about this. This could happen and if people don't start banding together it will. Over 10 or 20 per cent of farmers in a year or two will go under. If a guy is already on the verge of quitting it only takes another straw on his back to say: "Well, this is the end of it. I'm not fighting anymore."

BILL HENDERSON   Few people realize that the Peace River Valley in northern Alberta is capable of vegetable production. Bill Henderson is one farmer who vouches that it is possible. On his farm near Grimshaw he cultivates 50 acres of vegetables and keeps an additional 575 acres in grassland and feed production for his 30 head of cattle. The cows are his insurance. "One thing I try to do is never be in debt to the bank for more than the number of cows I have."

Since the early part of the century gardeners have managed to make a go of it up north. The long hours of sunshine make up for the shorter growing season. The distance from major centres, however, makes marketing and labour the two major problems, according to Bill. But he says that since 1975 the Alberta Vegetable Growers' Marketing Board has helped to avoid the price cutting that once characterized the Alberta market. Still, finding a buyer and transporting the produce is up to the individual gardener.

Running a garden is labour intensive, with the hoeing, trimming, picking, and packing still largely done by hand. The two Mexicans that Bill has working for him crossed a continent to pick vegetables.

BILL: Gardening is a full-time job on its own. Marketing is another full-time job and when you have to do both as well as haul the distance we do, you're away half the time. That's why I had cut back to 50 acres in vegetables, from 100. I sold very little in Edmonton last year — no corn at all and maybe six loads of cabbage and turnips. I sell as much as I can at the farmgate and to the wholesalers in Peace River and Grande Prairie.

It's in the mind of most people, including government officials, that the place to garden is the south. There are some things that we grow really well up here that they can't grow in the south and vice versa. We can't grow netted gem potatoes out here because they get knobby. But we can grow cabbage and keep it green till Christmas while the cabbage coming out of the south at that time of the year is white — the same cabbage. Maybe it's our long hours of sunshine or maybe it's cooler in the fall when we're harvesting.

So, when people say there's nothing north of Edmonton, it doesn't sit very well with us. We've been here a long time. There were vegetables being grown here in 1919. I don't think there has been a year that there hasn't been vegetables on this place. That should prove it.

There were 17 gardens along the river when I first got here in 1957 and some of them were just two or three acres with a bit of surplus. But, there were 25- and 40-acre gardens too. Some gardeners retired, others sold because they couldn't put up with the headaches. Now there are two or three of us but there could be a lot more. I think if there was a proper storage and packaging point with a good manager who could market for gardeners, and some assistance with buying or renting machinery...because all equipment is so expensive now...the land is here and possibly people might start going back into it.

I suppose we are too dependent on imported vegetables. I've talked to growers in California who can hire an entire Mexican family — you know, wife, kids, everybody — for 500 dollars a month. It costs me over six dollars an hour for my Mexican help. I pay them four-seventy-five an hour and I buy their round-trip airfare before I even see them.

If you're a small gardener, with maybe five acres, you can sell most of your produce at the gate or you can take it to a farmers' market. But that isn't enough for a living so you have to get bigger and you have to start thinking about wholesaling. And once you start wholesaling, you get a little bit less for it because the wholesaler has to have a mark-up, so does the store, and there is freight involved.

That means you have to grow a lot more acres and, for a young gardener starting out, you're going to have problems selling your produce. The first thing the wholesaler is going to say, because he doesn't know you, is bring in a sample. And you can't really blame the wholesaler. He's already bringing in produce from California and knows what he's getting. It takes about five years to build up your reputation so that they know the quality and how you pack it and whether it is acceptable or not.

It's a gamble. If you have hail or frost there's no insur-

Francesco and Roberto, with Bill Henderson,
Grimshaw, Alberta

ance, at least if there is I'd like to know where to get it. You have a high investment before you even see the crop. Then there's labour problems. If I hire someone and he quits in July or August, how do I get my crop off?

One of the biggest reasons why I get Mexican workers is because a Canadian sees a better job and I suppose you can't blame him, he's gone. Whereas the Mexicans come, that's all they know. That's all they've ever done and they're good at it. I know when I hire them that they are going to be here for the summer and into the fall and my crop will be off before they leave. If they quit, they can't go to the neighbour and work. They have to go back to Mexico.

Before we can get Mexicans we have to advertise right across Canada through the manpower centre. Nobody wants to work in a garden. I don't know why, it's not hard work. I used to get school kids before I got Mexicans. That first week is really tough. You're bent over hoeing. Your back hurts and so do your legs, but after that you're away. The two I have here now work from seven A.M. to seven P.M. and take an hour for dinner. I just turn them loose and they work whatever hours they want. One year, one Mexican was working 15 hours a day, but that was a bit much. They decide on their own. A lot of them work Sundays.

Then too, sometimes we go fishing or to the country fair. I often take them with us. If they don't work for three days or something, because of rain for instance, they get fidgety. They start thinking of home. They'll tell you that their wife isn't well or that one of their children has been sick. They think about home when they're not working.

Some people think we shouldn't bring people in when there is so much unemployment. But if we advertise and nobody else wants the job, we have no choice. We have to hire them.

36

HARLEY MICHAEL farms a section of land near Alix, Alta., where he raises purebred cattle. In 1979 he was one of the organizers of HOPE (Heatburg Organization to Protect Our Environment), a group of some 75 farmers who rallied to stop a generating plant that would have displaced a number of them and put once productive land under water. HOPE petitioned government, attended hearings, and did whatever it could to make its point. As Harley says: "When someone is going to take your livelihood away I don't think your concerns are conjecture."

For a number of reasons the generating-plant project has been stalled and is unlikely to go ahead in the near future. Harley says that environmental groups in Alberta are letting industry know they are not going to accept industrial development without demanding answers.

HARLEY: The reason we founded HOPE was for survival. It was at the time that Fording Coal, Alberta Power, and Calgary Power were proposing an export power project and it entailed the strip mining of more than 12,000 acres of land. It was a thermal generating plant to generate power to export to the northwest United States — all part of the western power grid. Had it been necessary to develop that power for use in Alberta or Canada we would have looked at it in a little different light.

There are few things that we can get without giving. And we felt that to lose productive agricultural land couldn't be justified. We felt that maybe in a short period of time the world would have a hard time feeding itself. Statistics show that about 13 per cent of Canada is capable of producing food. Out of the other 87 per cent there might be a more suitable area for industry. It doesn't make sense to cause destruction and problems with reclamation, problems with acid rain from the burning of coal to generate power, and problems with water quality.

It all comes down to a dollar value in the end. What are we willing to pay for that power and what are we willing to sacrifice to get it? I think we still waste a lot of power. I have a problem when I drive through a city at night and see of-fice buildings with the lights on at two o'clock in the morning. Is that necessary? Shouldn't we save some of that power? Do we really need to generate more power?

The land is class two to five around here — with five considered the lowest quality. What's prime agricultural land? If I can produce as many dollars on class five with purebred livestock as someone else is producing on class two or three with grain, can you explain to me which is prime? If handled properly, class four can produce. The difference is that your options are not as great.

I have no quarrel with some industries locating on class four or five. But to destroy 12,000 acres with a plant which is one of the worst causes of acid rain in the world — how many acres of land not directly affected by the coal-generating plant would be affected by pollution? I will accept industry when we put it where it will do the least amount of damage that it can and when we clean its act up so that it doesn't pollute what's around it.

I think we have to have a more cautious approach to things, especially when it comes to agriculture. I think our whole society has been going at breakneck pace and maybe we've broken a few too many necks. Maybe we should do more testing on some of these things, chemicals for instance, and slow down a bit.

The economics of farming creates a lot of problems. It's hard to quit farming the dollar because the bank manager comes around every once and awhile for payment. If we can bring our costs closer in line with what we are getting for our product, it would help. I don't have any doubt that Canadians will pay more of their income for food in the future than they have in the past. It has to come. Look at the rest of the world. I think we have to get down to worrying about what it costs for the "necessities" and not the "niceties."

I think one of the biggest problems is that we are facing a subsidized world. You look at the subsidization of agriculture in other parts of the world...it's tremendous. And basically in Canada we don't have subsidization of the farmer. We have the subsidization of the consumer and we have a cheap food policy that demands votes. The federal govern-

Harley Michael,
Alix, Alberta

ment is looking for the votes in Quebec and Ontario and they are urban-based.

Somehow we have to educate people about where their food comes from. When I don't produce, maybe when I refuse them the food, maybe that will be the only way I have left to say: "Hey, I'm here. I've got a place in this world. I deserve to be here. And you'd better recognize me or you don't eat." Farmers may decide that farming the dollar is not worth their while and they can live without working for others.

What I would tell people about agriculture is that when it comes down to the bottom line, we supply the energy that is the most important in this country and that's the energy that runs the human body. And that energy crisis will be the greatest energy crisis that this world has ever seen. It will make oil look like peanuts. That's the point that they should start to listen to. And that could come within 20 years.

THE UNRECOGNIZED RESOURCE

Initially, Colleen stares blankly when I ask her what issues she is concerned about as a farm woman. She's been so busy that she hasn't stopped to think about it for awhile. She reflects, scratching her forehead under the diaper she has recycled for use as a bandana. And then the words come rushing out....

Susan rushes to the house carrying two large pails of fresh milk. Her troop of three children trail behind in single file, trying to keep up to mom's fast pace.

Kathy, who has just returned from bringing the men's lunch out to the field, washes the dishes while trying to keep her eight-month-old occupied. He's taken up a seat in the extra sink, plays with a spoon, and watches mom. Finished that clean-up, Kathy immediately begins preparing supper for the men. Once that's through she'll bundle up the baby, load up the truck with yet another meal, and head off to the field.

Arlette is planting what seems like an acre of garden. At the same time she tries to keep her brood occupied by letting them transplant the odd tomato, watching closely to make sure the tomatoes are not maimed in the process. Only another ten rows to go....

Women have worked the land as long as men. Farming is one of the few occupations in which women have not had to fight to share the work. They have, all along, been prime supporters of the family farm, both within the home and in the field. Yet the word farmer is synonymous with the male gender. Its mention does not arouse the vision of a woman hard at work during seeding or harvest. Women do farm but by and large in society's eyes they only farm by association and rarely are they referred to, or even identify themselves, as farmers. Women on the farm are called housewives, farmwives, or farm women, but rarely are they called farmers.

The title given to a person's occupation often reflects how a person is perceived and rewarded. On the farm, women, and often their children, are an invisible labour force — one that isn't taken into account when a tally is made of the sweat that goes into food production. For farm women, lifestyle and economics meld into one as fieldwork, housework, child care, and leisure hours revolve around the farm operation. As women the prime issue is much the same as their husbands' — sustaining the family farm. It is through the financial difficulties of the family farm that women's issues must be viewed.

When the farm cannot afford to hire an extra hand, it's the farm woman who gets out into the field to drive truck, combine, swather, or tractor. Farm women run errands, keep the books, care for the animals, work in the fields, grow gardens, can fruit and vegetables, raise the kids, and do the housework. It is only in the last decade that research has begun into determining the exact contribution that farm women make to the farm operation. There is still a lack of information, but a few recent surveys point out that farm women do it all and do lots of it.

One of the most recent and detailed surveys, conducted by the National Farmers Union in 1982, shows that of the more than 200 women members surveyed, each works on the average 81 hours a week. From spring through fall, farm women spend about 31 hours a week doing farmwork and 41 hours at housework. Farm women do 85 per cent of household tasks and 16 per cent of farmwork. According to the survey their spouses, on the other hand, average 7 per cent of the household tasks and 65 per cent of the farmwork.

While many farm women carry a double workload, a large chunk carry triple. About 31 per cent of farm women are employed at off-farm jobs — 22 per cent full-time and 9 per cent part-time. On average these women contribute over a third of the total family income. And while a large number of women work off the farm to help maintain a standard of living eroded by input costs, both the NFU survey and another in 1979 by the Council for Rural Development Canada show that between 12 and 30 per cent of rural women would like to have wage work if they could find it.

According to the NFU study the same percentage of men work off-farm as women but, in keeping with society's double standard vis-à-vis earning power, male salaries contribute 61 per cent of the total family income. Interestingly, farm women are better educated than their husbands. Of the women surveyed by the NFU, 23 per cent have post-secondary education while only 10 per cent of their spouses do. One of the reasons why women are better educated is that, in a bit of twisted irony, they are encouraged to become so. After all, sons become farmers, daughters do not.

This stereotyping, which encourages rural women to seek their fortunes outside of rural communities, creates problems in other areas as well. Statistics Canada figures show that there are more than twice the number of single men on farms as women. That presents serious lifestyle and economic problems for the family farm. While farm women's work is unrecognized in monetary terms, a farm without a woman is much more difficult to manage, let alone to share and preserve for future generations.

The toll of having to subsidize the farm through other means, coupled with trends towards specialization and mechanization, forces the farm family into making labour-saving decisions. There is less time to work in the farm's own garden — traditionally the woman's job. The farm unit's food self-sufficiency often suffers. While the average urban family paid $3,226 for food in 1978, the farm family paid only slightly less at $2,823. In trying to produce for the market, farm families don't have time to produce for themselves and have turned into consumers.

Recent income-tax law changes, introduced in 1980, allow for the possibility of unincorporated farms to pay a

Zoé Nisbet, Ardoch Co-op Farm,
Success, Saskatchewan

farmwife's wage if she works in the field. Household tasks, of course, are not considered contributions to food production by the government. Still, only 21 per cent of farm women are paid for farmwork. The red tape involved in claims is a major hindrance. As well, as the NFU study points out, more than half of those surveyed reinvested between 75 and 100 per cent of their total family income in the farm. In other words, sustaining the family farm is a tough balancing act and women are, in their effort to preserve the family farm and lifestyle, not included in the costs of production.

Farm women's work also goes unrecognized when it comes to social services. Farm women, because few earn wages, have limited old age security and are excluded from pension plans, unemployment insurance benefits, or worker's compensation schemes. For the most part support systems such as crisis centres, counselling, and legal aid services or day care facilities do not exist. Farm women are often isolated and left to cope alone with whatever they encounter, whether it be alcohol and drug problems, wife battering or marital breakdown.

The impression among farm people is that as the farm crisis intensifies so do the social problems triggered by stress. While there is still little research available regarding farm finances and stress, a study done in Ontario entitled "The Farmer Takes A Wife" concludes that there is a direct link. This survey of farm women in Bruce and Grey counties reported increases in insomnia, alcoholism, and physical abuse. The women surveyed also reported increased hostility, depression, and thoughts of suicide, all due to burgeoning debt loads.

In many rural communities it is even difficult to find competent medical attention. The NFU survey noted that 47 per cent of the women listed health as a major concern within their families and cited problems such as allergies or respiratory and back problems.

But farm women aren't complainers and few are prepared to sing dirges. They've become accustomed to handling life on their own. Almost all of those surveyed in the NFU study said they were satisfied with the tasks they perform on the farm and most were fully or generally satisfied with the lifestyle. But these same women were doing more than dropping a hint when well over half of them jotted down that they were dissatisfied with the recognition they receive from society, particularly in the concrete area of social benefits.

Farm women have been silent for a long time and while they are now slowly beginning to organize within farm groups, it's unlikely they'll ever create much of a storm. They are just too busy trying to keep the family farm together. They also see quite clearly that their lot and fate, as well as that of their families, are tied directly to the lack of a fair return on their products. They see the results: fewer farms, further isolation, the loss of hope for improving services, and a standard of living that in general is eroded. The exploiter, as many point out in these interviews, is in fact an entire society that refuses to recognize their role in food production.

Sherry and Jessie Lucas,
Bluesky, Alberta

44

JEANNE-MARIE CROZIER was raised on the farm. She left for the city after high school and trained as a hairdresser before returning to the land as a farmwife. I met her for the first time when she cut my hair in her salon in Biggar, Sask. She was wearing a yellow cotton dress — the kind used in advertising campaigns to romanticize about picnics in the countryside.

But farming is no picnic in the countryside, as Jeanne-Marie knows. By day she operates her own salon, which provides half of the total annual family income. The other half comes from the five quarters she and her husband farm. Jeanne-Marie keeps 100 head of sheep — "a fair few" — and handles 50-pound bags of chop, takes care of the books, and averages about 80 hours a week working.

JEANNE-MARIE: Women don't option to farm. They marry farmers and come back to the farm like I did. I thought I was marrying a carpenter, not a farmer. I thought I'd rot out here. I really enjoy it now. For awhile, living in the city was prestigious. People from the country thought you were "just fine" if you lived in the city. That was important for a period of time, but it became unimportant. The city was boring. I didn't have my own space. I wanted something a bit different, something a little more risky, and farming is definitely risky.

The first difficulty is not just dealing with one man, your husband, but with perhaps four men from your husband's family. You're dealing with egos because when you start wanting to farm yourself you have to deal with men who don't want to be misplaced by a woman. If you're afraid of bruising egos, you don't do anything. And that's tough.

The men don't know how to act with a woman around. I mean, do you still swear? Where do you urinate when there's a woman around? It's new to them.

I hear myself saying, because they're saying, because my father said: "You can't do it." And me agreeing and saying: "See they're right. I can't do it." So, it's really scary and tough. Right now I don't handle the egos. I don't take part in any of the seeding or harvesting rituals because I go to work away from the home.

My goal is to pay for the house and then in a few years I want to be at home and farm. I want to farm — there's more of a challenge to it. I learn a lot more. It's good to get down to basics again and work with your hands.

The thing that bothers me is that no work seems as important as being out there seeding or harvesting. The truth is that we wouldn't be able to farm if I wasn't working — not feasibly. We sat down and figured it out. The farm would put food on the table, heat the house, but nothing else. Yet my work doesn't seem important to my husband's family. It's just like I'm playing at it and when I'm tired I'll be a housewife and have children.

You know, I can't think about the amount of work I do because I wouldn't be able to do it if I did. I don't think about it. I just take lots of deep breaths and do it.

Jeanne-Marie Crozier,
Biggar, Saskatchewan

IRENE NIMMONS farms a section of land near Didsbury, Alta., and has farmed alone for the past 30 years, since the time "when I got left widowed." She lives in a house that was built in 1900. Until 1977 she was "lugging in water and lugging it out." Her farm is called "Retrospect and Prospect," which she translates into respect for the past and hope for the future.

Irene says she has a good life, and she doesn't complain even when she discusses an average annual income that never exceeds $3,500. Now, in her sixties, she has taken out the first bank loan of her life — a loan of $250,000 so that she can farm the land her father farmed before her.

IRENE: The thing about farming is that you always have to be prepared for the unexpected. But I've enjoyed it, more so as I'm getting older. At first it was an endurance test not quite being familiar with the machinery and the responsibility. The manual labour was the hardest thing. I guess I was determined. My son was really excellent beyond the average. I stayed because of him. He was 13 when my husband was killed. I knew if I gave up the farm he'd never have the opportunity if he so desired to farm. I didn't expect it of myself, but I did it. The neighbours came in to help the spring my husband was killed.

Getting the loan recently was difficult. I don't think the bank really believed I was farming on my own. The bank manager came out here and saw me swathing. Then he could more or less believe it even though he had known me for years. I hope that I continue to enjoy farming now that I have this debt. If you have to pay high debts and high prices you can be forced into mining the soil. I have to tidy up my money to buy this land...maybe I'm being suckered.

I put myself into any job that has to be done. The only thing I don't like doing is branding, particularly alone. Now a former hired-hand comes to help me. He brings his family and we have a day of pleasure. It's not hardship to me anymore.

I don't like the large farms. The people who run them are not concerned about the schools and the affairs that are going on in the community. I think the social life is as im-portant for people as the other aspects. I don't think I'm as lonely as a lot of married women would be coming out here. I'm an "old-timer" on the farm, you might say. I'm going to farm as long as I feel good, as long as I feel satisfaction. When I go on a holiday I'm always anxious to get back into the harness again and do it. I feel like I fit here.

If I left I'd miss the soil and probably a whole lot more. I think the soil has power. You put a seed in the soil and look how it grows. Isn't it fantastic? Don't you think so? No matter what, nobody can manufacture the soil in the same way and give it the life. I hope that people continue to live off little patches of land.

Irene Nimmons,
Didsbury, Alberta

ULLA DE BRUIJN was part of the first agricultural exchange organized between Canada and Denmark. She was also one of the first women to attend agricultural school in Denmark. For the past three years she has farmed a half-section mixed farm in central Alberta on her own and has vowed to remain on the land to raise her four children.

"I'm not looking to build up a dynasty. I limit myself. I want to raise my kids on the farm and get them off to a good start," Ulla says. She pulls out her books to show me how she keeps track of all aspects of her operation: everything from the amount and kind of fertilizer or chemical used on a particular field to the price per pound for a dressed animal on any given day of the year. She is a small, sturdy, intensive operator.

ULLA: I look at myself as a farmer who is a woman, not as a woman who is farming. I think one of the reasons I took the farm over was that a good friend of mine — he farms with his family six miles from here — when I was talking about maybe taking it over and trying to make it go, he said: "Oh, sure you can do it." And that's really what gave me that push. You need someone who believes you can do things and you'll get it done.

The first year I was nervous about putting in my cropland. This year, already, I am much more confident. I looked into it more. Being a "girl" in farming, I have always had to compete with these young, strong "boys" and I've always had to use my head every time they used some muscle. I've always been proud of doing that. For example, I use my front-end loader a lot more, rather than carrying things. I use big round bales because you can use machinery to stack them. I use a garden tractor with a wagon to carry chop pails.

Overseas, when I started farming, it was accepted that a girl who wanted to do a rare job could do it. That acceptance was not here when I came to Alberta. I saw a lot of women who did quite a bit of work on farms — like the milking — but when neighbours came over the women quickly ran into the house and got combed up and pretended they had never really done very much outside. I feel that you can just as well be honest and say: "That's my job."

All the years I can remember farming has never been a good business so it doesn't scare me as much although now it seems harder than ever. The only thing you can do is be as professional as you can. The income, if you take it in dollars and cents, is well below poverty level. But, if you keep your expenses down, have a garden and some meat, you don't starve. My income is three or four thousand dollars a year. Something like holidays we don't take and driving a new car has never existed.

I feel more discrimination as a small farmer than as a woman. I remember once I took some beef to market in Red Deer. The packer offered me 75 cents and I know they were offering the big feedlots over one dollar. When I argued, they would only put it up to 85 cents. For them I didn't have enough cows. I wasn't dealing in the kind of volume that large farmers were.

Ulla De Bruijn,
Ponoka, Alberta

Marie Scott has farmed alone for 13 years and raised six children on the land. She operates 11 quarters north of Palo, Sask., where she keeps 50 cows and an assorted number of sheep, chickens, ducks, and geese.

Marie doesn't find her situation unusual. It's all very normal. Nor does she talk about sexism or discrimination. She does recall that in the early days of farming alone, the lifting of 70-pound bales caused her shoulders to widen: "I began busting out of my shirts and coats." And she admits that at times it might have seemed odd to observers to see her returning from the hairdresser's, all done up for a local social gathering, only to have to rush off to the barn to deliver a calf.

Marie: It has been hard. But times go fast when you're busy, so I've really kept busy. Oh, the house isn't clean all the time. First things first. When we're busy, if I get six hours of sleep I'm doing good.

To me sitting on a tractor is relaxing. You have one thing to do, not a hundred. I've always done farmwork, so people around here were used to me when I began farming alone after my husband's death. Still, there were lots of suggestions that I should leave.

I've seen some discrimination...just a bit. I had problems with life insurance. When they found out I was doing outdoor work on the farm, they said my policy was not legitimate. I suppose they thought I'd probably get hurt driving all that "big" machinery. I also had a problem getting a permit book from the Canadian Wheat Board. They weren't going to give me one because they didn't think I was the operator. The local elevator agent soon set them straight.

It's getting really hard to start farming with the land prices going up and up. My son Joe is starting out and using most of my machinery. He has a long way to go, but that's what he wants and he's not giving up at trying to get what he wants.

One of my main concerns is chemicals and the damage it does to the land plus to the people who use it. You know, I've sprayed for 30 years now and I feel that my respiratory problem is coming up.

Actually, a farmer isn't rich until he's dead because what you've got is all invested. Farm machinery doesn't seem to stand up anymore. We have an old tractor that's 35 years old and you give it one flip of the crank and it goes. The others will never last that long.

Marie Scott,
Palo, Saskatchewan

SHIRLEY BARRACK has farmed on her own since she was widowed in the mid-1970s. Sitting at the kitchen table on her farm near Cereal, Alta., she chuckles as she recalls the difficulties that she had learning the ropes. She says that foolish mistakes were made, but she firmly believes that men make as many mistakes, at least in the beginning. They just don't talk about it.

Shirley says that farming is more relaxing these days, although finances always create difficulties. But she has gained the confidence to be a farmer and wonders what all the fuss was about trying to decide whether she could do it.

SHIRLEY: People look on the farm as an easy way of life, but it isn't. For the first 12 years of our marriage we got hailed out 10 times. We had enough to eat, but it was tough slugging. We'll never be rich, but we'll never starve either. That was our motto.

When I first started farming alone I didn't think I could do it. But I did. Most people thought I'd go down the tube, but I didn't. I think most people thought I was crazy, and because they thought I was crazy I guess I tried harder. The farm is the only place I wanted to be. When my husband died I promised him that I would give it my best shot. He hoped all of his life that we would have a 30-bushel crop. And then, two years ago, on one field we had a 30-bushel crop. He would have loved to have seen that.

In the beginning it was tough, sure. You do stupid things you know. The first time I just about wiped out the entire yard when I was trying to use the swather. But I would do it all again regardless of the ups and downs. It's rewarding when you do all these things and you come up on top. It's rewarding if it doesn't disappear on you. The first couple of years I probably worked myself to death. You have to adjust. You're trying to make good.

You have to like working with your hands. You have to like making something out of nothing and you have to be tolerant of going without things. Farming is a way of life. We are different from urban people. The difference is that we think in terms of generations.

It's hard to watch family farms go. I think the reason is that farming is getting to be too commercialized now. Everything is getting so complicated. It used to be that when something went wrong with your tractor you pulled it apart yourself. You can't do that anymore.

Shirley Barrack,
Cereal, Alberta

54

PAT KEYSER has farmed for the past seven years near Landis, Sask. She calls herself a feminist farmer and has spurned traditional rural life by co-habiting rather than marrying. She was one of the first women to graduate with a two-year diploma in agriculture from the University of Saskatchewan and has been involved in national and provincial Status of Women groups. Pat operates all of the farm equipment but concedes that she doesn't like to seed.

Revenue Canada audited the farm three times, says Pat, and because she is officially "employed" by the farm and receives a salary, the main question seemed to be whether she worked indoors or outdoors. "If I were a man they wouldn't dare ask."

PAT: Rural people are changing a lot. I don't know if it's necessarily for the good. There has always been this idea that we have to be more like city people. You know, there's always that quote: "Oh, that's such a farmer thing to do" or "Don't act like such a farmer." It's a real putdown. So we all want to be sophisticated and "dine" at seven-thirty in the evening. We're really trying to be more like city people and it's all so superficial.

I don't think it's possible for a woman to farm actively and have children. Where do you put the kids — in the sink? It's dangerous to take your kids out there. People don't really understand day care. They've always done without it. I don't have any children, but I think there's a real need for child care. Now, you can ask almost any rural woman or man if they need child care and they say no — you know — "The little missus stays home with the kids."

I farm. I don't say I'm a housewife. I guess maybe one of the reasons I call myself a farmer is that I think in order to call yourself a housewife you have to be married...not necessarily to the house...but to a man. And I'm not married.

That's been an issue in my life...you know...what are you? Let me tell you about "farmerette." I farmed with my father for a couple of summers and people called me "farmerette" — so trivializing. I once wrote an essay in university about what would happen if Betty Junior decided to take over the farm. I remember once when a neighbour of ours was out walking with his three-year-old son, and this woman was heard to say: "He's just going to be such a good little farmer." And I just know it's not said about his sister.

I grew up on the farm, but I never did much farmwork. If dad was really stuck for help I might pitch in and hold "whatever." There was never any expectation of the girls farming. I think my dad was disappointed that he had three daughters and no sons to pass the farm to. Leaving my dad's farm caused me a lot of trauma. I felt guilty about that for a long time.

There was a lot of pride in that thing of passing something on. I really think it's sad that women aren't looked on as potential farmers.

Pat Keyser,
Landis, Saskatchewan

Going, Going, Gone

Mike's face drops as he hangs up the phone. He turns to his wife and says simply: "They're on their way." It's the moment that both have been dreading yet planning for during the last several months. A few quick calls later and neighbours have been rounded up. They'll rally at the farmgate within minutes, with any luck before the receiver gets there.

When they get to the gate, the farmers remove keys from ignitions and abandon ownership of the vehicles in an effort to stymie the receiver. No one lets on whose truck is whose. When the receiver goes back to town to check on registrations and warrants for forceful removal, the farm survival group replaces the first vehicles with other ones, and the process of getting warrants and checking registrations begins again.

The farmers know that these kinds of actions are short-term solutions. They are an effort to pressure the banker to renegotiate. Mike knows that too. He doesn't want his neighbours to face obstruction charges so if push comes to shove he'll open the farmgate.

Some farmers, knowing they can't block the farmgate eternally, decide to use other tactics. Some have removed fan-belts from equipment or taken the air out of tires. In the winter some have frozen tires to the ground with boiling water or removed rotors from the motors. An angry farmer might remove crucial nuts and bolts from his equipment to lower its sale price. An urban receiver won't notice the mutilations until too late.

There are other tactics as well. Once the equipment is taken farmers may organize penny auctions. Activist farmers will corner the auctioneer hired by the receiver and intimidate him into silence. A supportive farmer will take his place on the podium and only accept bids from farmers identified by armbands or some other marking. The machinery will be bought back for the bankrupt farmer with pennies.

The inception of the Canadian Farm Survival Association is a good example of farmers channelling their frustration and anger into collective action. The same attitude that has pressed them to continue farming despite low incomes is the same one that pushes them, in some cases, to defy the law. Farming is a way of life. Many of them see it as a hard-earned right.

In 1982 there were 78 farm bankruptcies on the prairies, 410 across the country. A year later farm bankruptcies on the prairies doubled to 154, and by the end of 1984 had increased yet another 33 per cent. Increasing land prices paved the way to bankruptcy for many farmers. The stage for the vicious cycle of inflationary land prices was set with the 1967 Bank Act amendments. Those changes allowed banks to enter into real estate mortgages for farms, homes, and businesses, and eliminated ceilings on interest rates, which had been previously set at 6 per cent. As if on cue, the banks began offering farmers increased loan amounts and, concomitantly, land prices began to spiral. As farm debt across Canada increased so too did bank profits, jumping from $491 million in 1970 to $2.1 billion in 1981.

But bankruptcies, although reaching record heights, only tell part of the story. They do not include all foreclosures or count those farmers who have sold out or left quietly, knowing that a fight with the banker would not stop the loan interest from accruing during what could be a lengthy court battle. The farm survival groups on the prairies estimate that one out of every two farmers under the age of 45 is in financial trouble while one out of four over that age is having cash flow problems. Most farm groups believe that the problems of the early 1980s are only the tip of the iceberg.

But neither statistics nor farmgate defence actions say

anything about the personal trauma that the farm family faces, the marital breakdowns caused by financial pressure or the children emotionally upset by events they can barely comprehend. The numbers do not tell of the loss of self-esteem, or the self-degradation that all too often overcomes and weakens the spirit when a farm is lost.

Hindsight is 20-20 and while farmers know that land prices, interest rates, and bad weather can all serve to do them in, they also search their memories trying to figure out what could have been done differently. Once they have gone through that file they sift through examples of other farmers in a similar position. As individuals they often end up with the inevitable question: why me and why now? No matter what the personal crisis, instinct dictates that there must be a reasonable answer and the search for one continues.

The radio is blaring and the press announces that the Minister of Agriculture is once again saying that it takes good management and good business sense to be a good farmer. Those who are bad managers just can't hold on anymore. Production and expansion mean progress and bad managers can't cut it. It's tough but it's necessary.

Funny, thinks the farmer, the banker told me that same thing not so very long ago.

The case of Roger Fleming, a fourth-generation farmer near Millet, Alta., is typical. Roger's problems began in 1978, the year after he had borrowed $600,000 to expand his dairy and grain farm into beef cattle. The cost of Harvestores alongside the inevitable building delays — combined with economic and natural factors out of his control — threw the farm into deep financial problems. During the course of the loan, interest rates fluctuated from 10 per cent to 20 per cent, or $60,000 to $120,000 in annual interest. When falling land, cattle, and grain prices coincided with a bad crop year and rising interest rates, Roger could not meet his payments.

Roger Fleming's debt to equity ratio no longer made sense to his creditors and in 1980 the bank moved. At the time he was less than $70,000 in arrears. By spring 1983, following three years of procedural wrangling in the courts,

Roger owed an additional $300,000 in interest. That figure rose to $370,000 once the court decision had been made. The decision made Roger and his family temporary tenants of the bank.

At this point both Roger and the bank were losers. The battle cost everybody. Similar cases have happened again and again to bankrupt producers on the prairies. The figures and details vary, but more and more farmers, in making great efforts to increase production — and the "viability" of their farms — are losing out and going under.

Farmers have to shoulder part of the blame for financial problems. But so do bankers and the government. The reasons farmers go under are as diverse as the soil types on the prairies. Laziness and mismanagement, while often cited as the main reasons for failure, are only superficial excuses. On every farm that I visited hard work, tough decisions, and external factors beyond the control of the farmer were at play. Some made mistakes. It's hard not to when loans are based on real-estate factors and inflated rates, and production is based on second guessing.

While most farmers try to appear indifferent when discussing the loss of their farm, few are. Farm women have told me about the difficulty of watching a man who can no longer get out of bed before noon. During my travels, I spoke with one farmer for hours, asking him how he felt, really felt, and received only unemotional responses. As I was preparing to leave his farm, he walked me to the car. His foot stubbed the tire several times as if checking for air pressure and he blurted out that, yes, he did get depressed at times. But then tomorrow would be better wouldn't it? All I could say was that I hoped it would be.

RICHARD ARNDT stands inside his empty barn near Arcola, Sask., discussing the financial downfall of the farm. In the midst of a sentence, as his eyes look out the barn-door towards the meadow, he stops, smiles, and points. "Look, see that doe coming out of the bush. She's going to cross that field and I'll bet there's a fawn trailing behind." The fawn appears, and our thoughts drift away as we watch in silence for a few moments. The two deer disappear nonchalantly over the crest.

Now, where were we? In his estimation was he a poor farmer? The seriousness of his response shows that he has thought about that question before. He did what was right at the time, or so he thought. The anger is gone, the loss accepted. In 1976, when Richard started farming, he had little idea that he would lose his dairy herd and his only quarter-section over a matter of $150,000 in loans and $4,000 in missed payments.

After trying to deal with the problems for several years, Richard gave up and called his creditors to begin liquidating in January 1983. The will was gone. But at age 34, he says, there's time to start over. At what, he's not quite sure. All that remained to be done was finalize the sale of the land and, possibly, of the house.

RICHARD: The farm is gone as far as I can see. It's gone. I can't see any way to hold onto it anymore. It would take a miracle to save it so we could still live here. That's about what it amounts to. We had bad luck, I guess. Things didn't work out the way we thought they would.

When we first moved here this place was a junkyard. We worked for years cleaning it out, hauling stuff out of here. Then we built our own barn with the help of neighbours. Everything we did we pretty well did by ourselves.

The problems started the first year of the dairy. I had allotted so much money for cows when I started and it took a year to build the barn because it took eight months to finalize my loan. By that time the price of cows had jumped and my budget was off. I was doing good though. I was going to buy a few more cows. The next year I got all bulls and no

heifers, I got a bad run on breeding. Then our cattle got sick. That was another bad year.

I got into dairy because I thought I was going to make it quick and easy, but it doesn't always work that way. When we started out our dairy cheque was about 3,000 dollars a month. But 80 per cent of the cheque went toward expenses. So when it starts to hurt you try cutting corners a bit and it only gets worse. You try to cut a few minerals out of the feed or something, but it doesn't work.

It hurts but I guess you can't stop. There's always tomorrow and you always have to have a roof over your head. You're still alive so you might as well keep right on going ahead. Now the hurt of losing our home has lessened. You know, it's something you worked hard for, something you dreamed of. We fought to get this place. I guess it's not all for naught. You always have to learn something through your travels.

A lot of people think it's mismanagement. I don't know what else I could have done differently, I did everything I thought was humanly possible to do. I never missed milkings and any time I ran into problems with the milk I took everything to the lab in Regina. No one's infallible. The only thing is that some are sitting on a higher chair than I am so they can point the finger.

They accused me of mismanagement. They got no feelings. They go by their books and there's no other way to do it. You get a guy out here who's 22 or 23 and he's never lost or fought for anything and he tells you what to do. Every day something happens and you could sit down and bawl. Then you tear in and and try to deal with the problem and it only seems that you make it worse.

I suppose I get depressed sometimes. But I get to thinking back…you know…we've always been provided for. We've had clothes on our back and food on our table and a roof over our heads. We've always had that luxury. It always seems when things get tough and you lose your position or you lose your job or you lose your farm, the next step has to be a little bit better. It seems to be an escalator. It's got to get better. It can't get worse because the bottom of the barrel's fallen out already. There's no use crying over what's gone.

Richard Arndt,
Arcola, Saskatchewan

ROGER FLEMING admits that he would have made a profit had he sold the farm when the financial institute he was dealing with tried to foreclose. The section 34-year-old Roger farmed since 1972 near Millet, Alta., had been homesteaded by his great-grandfather in 1899. As a fourth-generation farmer there was obviously more to lose than just money, and Roger decided to stay and fight it out.

Three years and countless court appearances later, Roger and his family, including his mother, are tenants of the bank. They no longer own the land their homes are on. The machinery and buildings, 400 head of cattle, and three quarters of land are gone. Roger's mother owns a quarter of land but it is essentially undeveloped. The Flemings plan to move there when the bank decides they should vacate.

ROGER: A good banker won't tell you how to market. He's the banker, you're the farmer, and you do your marketing. The bank I was dealing with tried to do it all. They did the forecasting. They had crystal balls. I was dictated to by them. They didn't figure that I could have a crop failure that would take me three years to catch up on. They also didn't realize that you couldn't cut your operation. I had to increase income. I had to increase my milk cheque. There was no way I could sell off dairy cows and pay the bills or lay off men and not get the work done.

We marketed cattle that should have been kept another month. A couple of times I kept cattle a little longer because they said the market was going to go up — and then it went the opposite way. That cost me money for buying feed.

The bank encouraged me to borrow money in 1977. I only wanted to put in one Harvestore but they said I should put in three to make it pay. The only problem is that when you borrow money from the bank they want 100 per cent plus back even though circumstances out of your control create the financial problems. They never want to take a loss even if it's their advice that created the problem. The bank should take the risk too.

Just because your equity is there doesn't mean that your pay-ability is there. My trouble was I was trying to be too effi-cient and it didn't pay to try and get the top yields. It didn't pay. I should have settled for 20 per cent less production and less input costs. We had top-yielding hay crops. We'd taken one cut off 110 acres and we filled a Harvestore that holds 800 tons. That's almost unheard of in this area. That was due to our fertilizer program, but we should have settled for a couple of tons less and cut the expense.

I blame myself in part for allowing it to happen. I didn't have to let it happen. It's not always best to be the good guy and be pleasant. I guess it doesn't hurt once in a while to voice your opinion and put your foot down. I shouldn't have let business interfere with personal feelings. They were all nice men. They never run me down. They were just men who were promoted into a position that they couldn't handle, much like myself. I took on tasks that I couldn't handle on the part of the banking end. I wasn't strict enough with the big business men that came in here to deal with me. I took them as friends instead of business people. And they were out with a latch to try and get my money.

It hurts. Everybody has a place in society. I'm a farmer. When the bank reported in one paper that it was misman-agement on my part, I take it that it was mismanagement on the business affairs and not mismanagement on the grow-ing of crops.

I'd always looked at farming as something you did for other people. Do I need to have 300 or 400 cows or 3,000 acres to put food on my table, to have a little money to travel? No, I don't need all that. You're not doing it all for yourself.

The banks are treating farmers like big-business gang-sters. They are treating farmers as if they have a large board of directors and all kinds of lawyers. That's what they think they are fighting. But they're just fighting people with a way of life.

They're changing our way of life. I would hate to see it change into large corporate farms, but I think it is going to. But, corporate farms are not most efficient. How can you beat a farm with all this cheap labour? If the bank had this farm they'd have been another million dollars in debt be-cause they would have had to pay labour...that is, if they'd paid the farmers as much as they pay the bank managers.   63

I'm not sure that the bank didn't do us a favour. I've been able to spend more time with my family and I've enjoyed doing that. I didn't realize that there was another life besides what I was doing. I never took time for my personal life other than doing things for other people. Holidays were very far between. The last time I'd taken a holiday was in 1975 after an injury. I was just working for others.

Roger and Jacquie Fleming, with daughter Elizabeth, Millet, Alberta

JOHN JAGO   In March 1983, when John Jago became president of the Manitoba Farm Survival Association, his own bankruptcy problems were on the horizon. When I spoke with him in late summer of that year he was about to harvest his two sections of land the same way they had been seeded — with the help of his neighbours. His cattle had long disappeared, so had his equipment, but he was still fighting for his land. He was $64,000 in arrears on a loan of $362,000.

John has been farming for 20 years near Reston, Man. When the receiver came he hadn't organized a farmgate defence. He hoped the financial institute would negotiate if conflict was avoided. But he admits it didn't make any difference. Since then he has attended a number of farmgate defences and says the tension in the air could easily ignite into violence. He doesn't want to see that happen, but he says it's almost inevitable when so many farmers are going under due to factors they can't control. Making a last stand for your farm is an emotionally wrenching experience.

JOHN: If you just sit in the house and say "To hell with it, I'm not going to do anything," then you don't leave them any choice but to foreclose. Now, if we had said that this spring when they seized our equipment and told us we couldn't use it to seed with, then the creditors would have no choice but to foreclose because I'm breaking my contract with them by not working and taking proceeds off the land. But, because I have a good bunch of neighbours, the support was unbelievable and we seeded the farm.

The problem with the farmer is that we're born and raised to work the land. We're not born and raised to know law. It's coming to the point now where the farmer damn near has to be a lawyer, because you sign papers at the bank and you don't realize what you've signed. You put your full trust in your manager. They could hand you anything and you'd sign.

The basic thing is that farming is a big gamble. When we went into debt we never foresaw the high interest rates. Nobody did. All we're blaming it on is the interest rate be-

cause when we borrowed that money we didn't borrow it saying that we weren't going to pay it back. We fully intended on paying it back.

In fact we worked seven days a week, year-round, to try and make it back. We had shed-cleaning operations, a custom bale-picking operation. We custom combined besides doing our own. All to make extra money. And everything we made we turned back into the Credit Union. We custom hauled cattle and water, anything to make an extra dollar to put groceries on the table.

What you build the whole thing on is hope that the price of grain and cattle are going to go up. The bank sold our cattle out in the last week of February for $400 apiece. The guy that bought them kept them right here, and calved them out for a month, and he had 46 cows and calves to take to market. He got $800 apiece for them. Why couldn't the bank have left us the cattle and let us double our money? These are some of the decisions that are made for you. I think they foreclosed on me because they thought I had equity left and they were going to come out of it clear.

Now I work for the Farm Survival Association and I deal with a lot of people. I know lots of people's financial problems and I know people who have a lot less security than I have and owe three times the amount of money that I do. They're not touching them at all. They have a lot of land, but the land's all leased. They have a lot of equipment, but the equipment is all leased. But if they were foreclosed on tomorrow there would be no hope of the financial institute coming out clear.

I think my problems have a lot to do with the fact that I'm the president of the Manitoba Farm Survival Association and the banks and the credit unions take a very dim view of the association. They wanted me to liquidate very quietly. I tried to deal with them all winter.

Something has to be done about it. If you start taking the farms away, what are they going to do with them? Who are they going to put on them? I maintain that they'll put a guy who's 25 years old on it and finance him to the hilt and three years down the road they'll do the same thing to him: foreclose. Then again they might lease it back to me.

You know, they blame this all on the individual farmer. But in this case here, it's not because we didn't work and you can ask any one of our neighbours. They put me down as a poor manager, but I had a neighbour say to me: "I knew exactly the day that you went into the Credit Union because of the way you started farming. You never farmed like that in your life."

That's the day I started farming everything as cheap as I could. But it didn't pay off. I was efficient, but I can't fight the interest rate and the price of grain. You give me control over the interest rate and the price of grain and what I pay for fuel and I wouldn't be in this position. None of us would be. It's just like working as an accountant all of your life. If you're born and raised on the farm, the longer you work at it, the better you get.

The financiers seem to have the attitude that they're going to show me. Let's face it, so far they have. But this time they've run up against somebody who is going to fight. I'm not going to quit without a fight. I told them two years ago the only way they'd carry me off of here was in a box. Well, I'm not going to go to the extremes of killing myself, but by Jesus I'm going to put up a fight. I'm not going to throw my hands into the air, despite all of the stress that goes with it. I'll fight it anyway I have to. But if the court says I have to go, then I guess I'll go.

A farmer is an eternal optimist. I guess the reason I'm fighting for this particular land is because I was born and raised just a mile and a half from here. I bought the first quarter in 1964 and the rest in 1969. Then in 1979 I bought my dad's section.

You never want to lose hope. If I lose the land, though, it will make me sit up and think about whether I want to go back into farming. Once you lose the grassroots farm it's never the same. The only way my young guy is going to farm is if I'm clear to help him.

John Jago and family,
Reston, Manitoba

THE NATURAL OR CHEMICAL WAY?

Towards the end of May the wheat plant enters what is commonly referred to as the four-leaf stage. The local chemical dealer is well prepared for the event. This is the time when the majority of prairie farmers begin spraying to rid their fields of wild-oats. For several months television advertisements have been priming farmers, using key words like deaden, kill, attack. Now the time has come to get the weeds.

It's Saturday morning at the chemical dealer's warehouse. Half-ton trucks back in and out. Sometimes their boxes are completely filled with five-gallon pails. Other times the farmers are more judicious, perhaps only buying five or ten. As they pick up their orders, some linger to chat about the latest techniques, auction sales, equipment prices, or the weather. Shop talk. Buying chemicals is occasion for an ad hoc social gathering.

As one farmer prepares to leave with his gallons I ask him jokingly, "So, how much did you empty your pockets of this time around?"

"Boy, it sure doesn't take long, that's for sure," he says, barely breaking step towards his truck. "Would you believe this is 25 hundred dollars' worth and it's not over yet?"

I follow him out to the truck. "Well, it must be worth it ... if the stuff works. Does it?"

"I don't know," he says, pausing by the truck's cab. "It seems that every year there are more and more weeds and they seem to be getting tougher and tougher to get rid of. But what else is there to do? You can't let them take over your crop."

A lot of farmers aren't sure whether agricultural chemicals are performing the job. Others are convinced they are. But in an economic climate where one bad crop can cause the downfall of generations of work, few are prepared to risk throwing out the sprayer. In fact, most farmers are using more chemicals than ever.

The use of agricultural chemicals has increased fivefold since 1940. For every North American four pounds of agricultural chemicals are used in the growing of food. In Saskatchewan nine pounds of herbicides are used for each individual. There are five million gallons spread over Saskatchewan annually. On the prairies 80 per cent of cropland is sprayed with 2,4-D or its derivatives. An additional 40 per cent is sprayed with wild-oat killers.

Often when a farmer has a problem with an unusual or a recurring weed, a local representative from Agriculture Canada is called in for advice. Once I sat at a kitchen table and listened to an Ag Rep and farmer discuss solutions. The Ag Rep suggested using a specific chemical. The farmer asked if there was another way, perhaps a less expensive way such as cultivation, to deal with the problem. The Rep appeared to find this question a little beyond the realm of possibility. "No, the chemical is definitely the quickest, surest way to kill that weed." The more money farmers owe, the less time there is to experiment and the more locked in they are to using the surest, fastest method: chemicals.

Prairie farmers are caught in a twisted, environmentally damaging, and expensive form of agriculture. They keep trying to soften the blow of low commodity prices by expanding their operations, taking on more and larger equipment, producing more and increasing supply, which in turn lowers the price of their product. As their farms get larger, they also have to face the problem of trying to juggle the additional workload. In an effort to increase volume, farmers have bought more and more artificial fertilizers and agricultural chemicals.

Meanwhile, while most scientists agree that it's impossible to determine the tolerance of the environment to chemicals, many believe we've reached the limit. The question remains: how much damage have we done? The monitor-

Picking up chemicals,
Davidson, Saskatchewan

ing of Saskatchewan water basins has proved that they contain residues of 2,4-D, 2,4,5-T, and other agricultural chemical products.

At the same time soil fertility is dropping. Scientists attribute the decline to a decrease in organic matter and nitrogen levels due to improper agricultural practices. In the last 70 years nitrogen levels in the soil have dropped by 50 per cent. In Alberta, seven times more nitrogen fertilizer is used than in 1970 yet it is estimated that by 1985 an average acre will produce 20 per cent less yield. Six million acres, an estimated 4 per cent of crop land in Alberta and Saskatchewan, are saline, or turning into salt, a condition caused by erosion or water drainage problems that allow once subsurface salts and minerals to rise to ground level. That figure is estimated to rise by 10 per cent every year. By the year 2000 topsoil will have blown or washed away to the tune of $8 billion worth of potential production. In the face of all of this it's wise to remember that to begin with, only 13 per cent of land in Canada is suited to agriculture and less than 5 per cent is prime agricultural soil.

And if all that is not enough, plants and insects are becoming resistant to the chemical controls that cost prairie farmers more than $250 million to purchase annually. A six-year study completed in 1983 by University of Saskatchewan biologist Dr. Jim Naylor shows that wild-oats, the major weed problem on the prairies, are becoming increasingly resistant to the two most popular forms of chemical controls, Avadex and Treflan. Naylor's study shows that in some fields, following four years of use, double and triple the amount of chemical was necessary to control wild-oats. There is also evidence to suggest that wild-oats, which are thus becoming resistant to common products, may also be developing a parallel tolerance to other chemicals. Naylor's findings on the prairies are consistent with studies from the United Nations Environment Program, which reports growing resistance to chemicals in hundreds of pests and plants around the world.

Perhaps the most troubling point is that it is impossi-

ble to assess the human cost of living in a sea of chemicals. In recent years a new disease called "ecological illness" has been recognized. Essentially this disease is a series of chemical allergies that often forces its sufferers to seek out food which has not been contaminated by chemicals in growth, processing, or packaging.

Even the concern of doctors, long known to be a fairly conservative group when it comes to ringing alarm bells, became evident in 1982 when the Canadian Medical Association passed a resolution on hazardous wastes, stating that both levels of government should promote policies to reduce dependency on potentially hazardous chemicals. The association resolution included a call to "prohibit the manufacture or sale of potentially hazardous chemicals that cannot be recycled or disposed of harmlessly."

Meanwhile, the Canadian Agricultural Chemical Association (CACA), which represents 53 Canadian chemical manufacturers, including Dow and Monsanto, increased its advertising and public relations campaign in 1982 to counteract the bad publicity. In so doing, the association admitted, albeit silently, a threat to their industry. The CACA has often been quoted as saying that agricultural chemicals are only hazardous if they are misused by farmers. "Read the label" is its common suggestion.

Industry spokespeople are quick to reassure farmers that chemicals are indeed necessary and that the industry has a financial commitment to food production. The research and testing of a new chemical costs about $25 million. The industry expects that global sales of each chemical will last for nine years at an annual return on investment of about 40 per cent for each chemical.

In March 1983 a spokesperson for CACA revealed that the global market for agricultural chemicals is $10 billion to $12 billion a year. The association is fond of saying that the Canadian market of $450 million to $550 million a year, most of it on the prairies, is a drop in the international bucket. Yet, when tackling environmental issues, past-President of CACA A.D. St. Clair was quoted as saying that concerned environmentalists are "under-informed activists" with "an unreasoning prejudice against the chemical industry." The association has also stated that chemical technology is a reality of food production and saves farmers from losing 30 per cent of their crops.

But research studies and experts have estimated crop loss would only be between 1 to 15 per cent if herbicides, which are 85 per cent of the Canadian agricultural chemical market, were not used.

Most farmers now say they are concerned about chemical hazards. After all, many handle the sprayers themselves and believe their health could suffer from the volatile substances. These days, however, there is an increasing trend among farmers to hire outside help when it comes to chemical applications.

The fear of chemicals is real, but no more real than the economic reality that spirals the need for production, expansion, and chemical use.

OMER AND ANDREA DEMEESTER are both in their seventies and have seen a number of changes in agriculture since they began farming in 1937. Although they are now retired, their interest in agriculture is still keen. They've passed the farm on to their son but still live on the land near Davidson, Sask. Their yard holds the legacy of three generations of used farm equipment: everything from old threshing machines to dilapidated Dodge trucks.

OMER: If a young man wants to start farming today I think it's pretty well out of the question with the price of farm machinery and land. We started farming with four old horses, a five-dollar drill and five-dollar plough and a set of harrows. We farmed that way for three years. We made out okay. We had no crop insurance, no hail insurance, but we made out okay. We got running water on our farm in the last two years, we never had it before. We hauled drinking water for years. It's a good life, farming is. It's a lot of hard work but we still like it. Hard work don't kill anybody as long as you get enough rest with it, I always say.

Things have changed quite a bit. We always came home for supper and for lunch — the horses had to be fed and have a rest. Some people are now going overboard. They work day and night, seven days a week. Back then we would give the horses a day of rest. The tractor doesn't need a rest. They have so darn much to do because they bought so much land. That's why the young guy can't get going.

If there is a half section for sale, the big guy will grab it. He has the financial backing. Then he has to work that many more hours to get done.

It's going to be all big farmers on the land and if they fail it's going to be corporate farmers. Instead of farming for yourself you'll be farming for them. I think small farmers are better for the country. These days there are a lot of young people who don't have jobs. No, I don't like it myself, all of these big farmers. There's no get-togethers any more in the communities. We used to get together at the schools for picnics. What is there now?

Years ago we didn't have chemicals. If it was a dry year all you got was Russian Thistle and junk...and still...all that poison ain't good either.

Used to be you'd never give an animal a needle unless he was sick. Now, even before you put them in the pasture — if you do put them in the pasture at all — there's a needle for this and a needle for that. And the feed is full of strange stuff these days.

Too much chemicals is used. I think that's why there are so many sick people nowadays. When you buy fresh fruit it doesn't have the same taste anymore. Nothing has the same taste anymore. I don't know if it's the environment, the air, or what that does that. The pork you raise yourself doesn't shrink up like the pork you buy over the counter. The chickens don't have the same taste anymore either. They are force-fed, you know. Everything tastes flat.

The farmers should lessen up on what they use, the antibiotics or whatever. This guy up here, one year he had flax and it didn't seem to ripen fast enough so he sprayed it so that it would ripen...for gosh sakes, eh!

Farmers would make a good living if they didn't have to put it all back into the farm. Now, if someone gets a few bad crops, they can't go on. If a man can't make a living on a section and a half something's wrong. Larger than that and they're just working for the machinery companies. There's a lot of land on credit...boy oh boy...

You know, even the eggs have changed. It used to be that everyone ate the yellow-yoked eggs. Now the yolks are so pale. All of the chickens are kept inside. I hate those pale yolks.

Andrea and Omer Demeester,
Davidson, Saskatchewan

EDDY CAMMER came back to the farm near Davidson, Sask., in 1973 after working on the oil rigs and putting aside money to purchase land and equipment. He had managed to acquire three sections and had visions of being a large farmer when in 1979 he discovered he had cancer. Despite his disease, he farmed his land for another year.

The disease went into remission but has had a heavy influence on how Eddy and his wife, Maureen, operate. Now they own seven quarters of land, much of it native grass or sown to perennial feed grains. Eddy cultivates about 60 to 100 acres every year and plans soon to take the strangely radical step of seeding, haying, and harvesting completely with horses.

The Cammer family, including a son, Milo, lives on a budget of about $4,000 a year. They keep cattle, make their own cheese, ice cream, yogurt, and butter. Maureen keeps a large garden and a milk cow. While they don't call themselves organic farmers, the Cammers have no use for chemicals on their farm. Eddy says he doesn't want to "bleed the land."

EDDY: I started using horses three years ago. It was mostly for fun to start with and then I got to liking it and I could see that they could do a lot of work and weren't very expensive to operate. So, I just started using them more and more. When I started I hadn't thought about it very much. I just thought it was something different. I wanted to drive four horses abreast like the older men always talked about. I wanted to drive tandem outfits like my dad used to talk about. I went to Manitoba to get some draughthorse colts. Now they're big enough to go to work, so they're going to.

Horses are a lot less headache. They don't get flat tires and they don't break down. You don't do as much, but it doesn't cost you as much so you don't *have* to do as much. We used to farm a lot more land than I do now, but I wasn't any better off than I am now. I worked a lot more. I spent more hours on the tractor. I was further in debt and I'm not now, so.... If a tractor breaks down a one-thousand-dollar bill is nothing. If a tractor tire gets a cut in it you're look-

ing at 500 dollars. Money is worth nothing anymore and you don't get much for what you grow.

Now I save on fuel, parts, and fertilizer and I save my tractor for the real heavy work. A horse doesn't put the stress on machinery that a tractor does. If something catches, a horse will give. There's no give to a tractor. The machine breaks because the motor just pulls it right through. You're also closer to your load so you can see what's going on better.

It's not as tiring to drive the horses for eight hours like it is the tractor. Maybe it's because of the noise. I know I can drive the horses for eight hours and I'm not played out like on the tractor, where my head is ringing and my eyes feel like someone threw salt in them. You're cramped in a tractor. You can't change positions and move around. With a horse you can get off and walk if you want.

It's hard manual work, but not overly hard. I don't mind. The stress from borrowing and being a couple of hundred thousand dollars in debt for machinery is gone. We were continuously taking out operating loans to buy fuel and machinery parts. In the fall you might catch up to some of it, then in the spring it was right back into the same thing. I never noticed it that much when I was doing it, but when I quit because of the sickness, I didn't want to go back to it. I'd had enough.

I had cancer four years ago — Hodgkin's disease. I wasn't supposed to do anything, but I still farmed all of that land for another year, then I just didn't want it anymore. Now I'm back up to 100 head of cows and that's enough. I don't want any more than just a living.

I can't go near sprays. My dad used chemicals. I can remember 2,4-D. They used to tell us we could drink the stuff. I can remember blowing the sprayer nozzles out when they would get plugged when I was 12 years old. I ran the sprayer. You weren't told it was deadly poison.

We wanted to get back to as natural a way of farming as possible. Sometimes in the spring I throw up just from the neighbours' spraying. It makes me nauseous. People just seem to be after the dollar. They're not leaving things for the next generation as they should be. Sooner or later we're going

Eddy Cammer,
Davidson, Saskatchewan

to pay for it because you can't keep taking and not give back. 75
It's just the way things are created. There's a proper balance
and if it becomes unbalanced you reap the consequences. You
can't farm half the country and not use chemicals. If people farmed smaller they could do it without chemicals.

I have no faith in government. The big guys line up on
one side and the little guys on the other and who do you think
the government tries to please? If they got rid of chemicals
and limited land size they'd be called communists by the big
guys. Yet, there's a lot of people out here who would agree
with that move.

In the end, though, the government does what gets them
the most votes. They don't care about agriculture.

BEN SWYSTUN's tractor looks different than most. Television-equipped tractors are rare. But as Ben is quick to point out, he spends from 70 to 100 hours a week on the tractor during peak periods. The television is a small investment for a bit of comfort.

Ben farms 2,700 acres, slightly over four sections, near Krydor, Sask., and estimates that his investment in equipment runs near $500,000. At one time he thought "the sky is the limit" but these days he's double-checking figures and reassessing the value of getting bigger. When I first chatted with him he was worried and wondered if he'd be around the next time I drove down the road. When I passed his farm again that fall Ben was smiling. A hailstorm had cut a wide swathe through his land. Heavy insurance coverage meant that he received more than if he'd picked up an average crop. A hailstorm took away the guesswork.

BEN: It's a very tough situation now. In my 35 years of farming I'm finding it the toughest right now. I feel that the inputs are very high — fuel, fertilizer, equipment, repairs, taxes — all are sky high and the prices of the product aren't as high. The last three years have been dry and last year we had hail that took much of our crop. I didn't insure too heavily so this really put me in financial straits, especially with the interest rates going up to 22 per cent. So I'm starting to hurt.

When the boys got interested in farming and we got a bit more land, we bought four-wheel-drive tractors, which are terrific on these hills. We started growing better crops. We were using a lot of anhydrous ammonia and we were hitting top yields. But in the last few years we've been losing a bit of ground, when it seems to me it should have been getting better. Now I'm getting older and rather than working with 10 or 12 feet of drill, I work with 36. The tension is a little bit higher.

When I first got my four-wheel-drive tractor I spent a lot of time on it. I've seen more sunrises than lots have seen sunsets. I wasn't one of those farmers who got a big tractor to work less hours in the field. I made damn sure that I used it for 600 hours a year or better.

After spending so many hours on the tractor I got something to take the monotony out of it. So I invested in a television set, and you know for awhile it was a novelty. But now I don't watch it much. It's surprising how rugged TVs were made. Sometimes I watch the soaps if I want to tease the wife, but mostly I watch the ballgames in the fall, or the hockey, and sometimes I even step on the clutch and throw it out of gear and sit and watch for a while. The TV is one of the cheapest things on the tractor.

But I don't think bigger is quite the way to go. If I had stayed farming with my sons we'd be farming close to 6,000 acres and for any person to manage that is extremely hard. If it really paid good it would be alright but when you feel you're fighting a losing battle, the pressure is really on. But what other way is there to go? I'm too young to sit on a bench in town.

If the energy prices were cheaper it would help almost immediately. My figures show me that with the inputs and the cost of land, the interest rates should not be higher than 5 per cent to make farming pay. Maybe that sounds low, but with the hills we have here I say that if wheat on level ground is worth four dollars, then mine should be worth seven. I've had trouble paying my interest bills and my taxes. I've kept up with my fuel bills and my fertilizer and I don't owe any personal bills. I owe the bank. I'm paying compound interest. I should have taken my father's advice and not borrowed money from a bank.

If I ever have to let some land go, part of my heart will go with it. You know every quarter of land means something to me. That's where we cleared, that's where we picked rocks, that's where mama brought the lunch....

But, I never learned to relax. If I go golfing or fishing I feel as though I'm stealing time. We never learned to play.

Ben Swystun,
Krydor, Saskatchewan

JOE SCHMIT   It's five A.M. and Joe Schmit pilots his spray plane up and down a field, leaving behind a mist of chemicals to control the weeds. It's dangerous work. Joe flies low, almost "right on the deck," within ten feet of the ground. In these early hours before sunrise, the soil and sky meld together in the darkness, making it difficult to judge height or see powerlines.

But despite the hazards, Joe has thrived on flying for years. Shortly after starting to farm near Davidson, Sask., Joe studied for his pilot's license. In 1965 he began custom spraying chemicals for farmers. He also operates as a charter operator under a commercial license. Joe makes no bones about it, flying was his first occupational choice. Farming came second.

These days Joe farms three sections and when not busy custom spraying, he hops on the tractor. He estimates that he spends $35,000 a year on fertilizer and chemical controls for his land. That's about $35 on every cultivated acre.

JOE: I think a lot of younger farmers have been given the option of so much money that they spend it foolishly. They went out and bought on borrowed money. Perhaps they needed it, perhaps they didn't. Many of them overspent. I think that's what's wrong with Canada. Our whole society says buy now and save later. Still, if costs continue to mount even the established farmers won't be able to hang on. Maybe the government will bail us out.

Sure there are people who own 27 sections, but there may be four or five sons on that land. I don't see land size as any kind of a problem. I think if they're productive, let them go at it. This is a huge country and you're not going to get that many people to live north of the 49th parallel and put up with everything that we put up with — the climate and all that. There will never be a problem in western Canada with an abundance of people because it's just too harsh a climate. They're going to live in Georgia or Alabama.

I think, in one simple word, the problem with farming is "government." There are so many regulations now in whatever you do. And it isn't just farming, but in my business of

flying and spraying there's more regulation all of the time.

It's getting so that we just about spray, well, if we had ice worms, we'd be spraying all year. We start about the first of May with fertilizers like urea and nitrogen. We'll spread seed, everything from rape, barley, alfalfa, and clover in the spring. Then we get into dry Avadex. Then we get into Liquid Avadex and Treflan. Then we get into seed spraying and pesticides. Then, in August, we may go up north around Humboldt and Melfort to spray for pesticides. Then it's harvest and into September.

That's when we are putting on Reglone to kill the crops. We use Reglone to desiccate a crop — to ripen it. It's a defoliant and it gets rid of the green. They're finding that with rapeseed, if you use Reglone, the pods will not pop open. It'll ripen quicker but the pod won't shatter. So, I think you're going to see more use of it. Then around October fifth, the sun is at such an angle that the earth doesn't warm up above 50 Fahrenheit and then we put on granular Avadex. Then the farmer can harrow it or leave it. It's fall-applied and aids the wild-oat control in the spring. In between I try to do my own farmwork when the wind is up. We go over our own land about four times with our aircraft sprayer. We do some chemical summerfallow so we don't have to go over with a tractor.

We have to have environmentalists, but the issue isn't the use of chemicals, it's the overuse. I think we have to have chemicals in order to produce cheap food. I don't think the chemicals concern me as long as the research is done on them. It's like fire...a lot of houses were burned down after they discovered it.

At one time farmers never sprayed. That was not too many years ago. Now there's only a few here and there that don't — the organic farmers. But the noxious weed act is going to be pounding on them because a lot of them are poor farmers in allowing their weeds to infest and blow around. Maybe we'll find out that some of these chemicals in two or three generations cause mutations. We don't know. But it isn't a riskless society. If you want a riskless society, you'd better not get out of bed in the morning. This is the way I look at it. I'm not concerned about the use of chemicals.

We don't know enough about these chemicals, but we're using them and when we do find out that they are harmful then we get rid of them and use something else. Probably the worse thing of anything I do is smoke. It's not the 2,4-D or the Treflan or the Avadex. It's the bloody cigarette.

I'd like to see my children farm, but like I've always said to them: "I don't care what you do as long as you do it well. If you want to be a bum be the best damn bum in the country." So, that's my philosophy.

Joe Schmit,
Davidson, Saskatchewan

HERBERT SCHMIEDGE's chemical dealership in Davidson, Sask., is a busy place on a late-spring Saturday afternoon. Farmers continually come and go, steadily purchasing the dealer's wares. Some farmers load entire half-tons full of chemicals, easily emptying their pockets of thousands of dollars. Others buy four- or five-gallon pails. The phone rings intermittently in the office adjoining the warehouse, where from time to time a group of men gathers to socialize.

After farming for more than three decades, Herbert quit in 1972. He'd operated almost every type of farm from hogs to cattle to grain and even did seed cleaning and custom spraying. But in the end there was more money to be had in selling chemicals.

Herbert calls the herbicides and fungicides he sells "real poisons," but adds in the next breath that farmers need to feed the world and that chemicals are the only way to do it.

HERBERT: None of my sons farm and it doesn't bother me at all. I think that it's real smart that they didn't go farming. It's a good life, you're your own boss, but there's no money in it. The larger farmer is going to get larger and the young fella is going to be an employee. It's happening all around. I don't like it at all.

About ten years ago we started selling the chemicals. We started small but in the last three years it's been fairly big. When the real boom is on there's days that we'll sell 15,000 dollars' worth of chemicals in an hour. We don't get no big profit off the top.

I get five or six semi-loads a year, about 700,000 or 800,000 dollars in a year is what I sell. We've had half-tons waiting to load up. When the real chemical boom is on it will go from six o'clock in the morning till ten or eleven o'clock at night. The boom is on when the wheat gets three or four leaves. Then again just before Christmas it booms again. The farmers want to stay out of income tax. I work on less profit. If you're too greedy you won't get the volume. I have people coming from 30 miles for chemicals because they know they can get them that much cheaper.

With my business, when the farmers get big enough they want to buy wholesale. Small businesses are going to be driven out. The real big farmer is no good to me at all. He doesn't even come to town. He goes down to the city and wants 200 cultivator-shovels and the factory sneaks him a deal. Farmers are trying to deal in chemicals, too. They want to buy wholesale. You can't have a town and have that happen.

I think the environmental situation is getting pretty tough. I think our soil is quite contaminated with chemicals. They're bringing in chemicals and they are trying to pretend that they are better, but they are just putting them under a different name. I can recognize the chemical by the few letters they add onto it. I know what it is and I talk to the manufacturer. It's pretty hard to say don't use it because that's why farmers are growing crops.

You see that wild-oat chemical that I was carrying today, well, that is making the farmer an awful lot of money. It's costing him an awful lot, but his good land would be a total loss if he didn't use it.

I'm at the end of my rope with chemicals, though. I do really think they bother my health from inhaling it all the time. I get headaches. I think it's bad for the lungs. My wife can't stand it. I do keep the doors in the warehouse open most of the time so that it draws right through. I use fans as well. I'm really concerned about the towns and the water supply.

A van came out here with a load of chemical on it for me and there was one that was dripping through the bottom. Now, supposing that was grasshopper poison. You can say it means nothing, but you take one grasshopper can that breaks on blacktop...how do you clean it up? I think it could end up in the water system.

I had a can break in my building in 1968 when we built this house. We had plasterboard sitting close to the can and some of the chemical went into the plasterboard and it soaked up the chemical. Then we built this porch with that plasterboard and you know, you can't keep a plant out in the porch. They still die from that. They die from that chemical smell, still. The tomatoes will wilt and die.

Herbert Schmiedge,
Davidson, Saskatchewan

You ask me how I feel about selling chemicals? Well, I feel 81
the same as the guy who was selling motorcycles told me he
felt and he finally had to quit too. He figured he was selling
a killing machine. That's exactly how I feel. Sooner or later
we are going to destroy ourselves with our own chemicals.

PROOF IN THE PUDDING

Avenge, Stampede, Round-Up, Sabre, Hoegrass, Heritage... any of these chemical items, as the jingle of one major manufacturer encourages, will "change the way you farm your land."

Organic farmers are convinced that agricultural chemicals have changed the way the majority of farmers produce food. They think that, rather than a positive change, the spurring of production through artificial stimulants sacrifices quality for quantity.

Most organic farmers are former chemical users. Often, the metamorphosis to ecological agriculture or non-chemical farm practices has been the result of a personal crisis. Some found themselves suffering from a health problem. In the search for the root cause of their own illnesses they stumbled upon the chemical link in food residues and decided that if the food wasn't fit for their consumption it was unfit for everyone's. Others became organic producers after hearing and investigating soil and water deterioration. Their's was a moral crisis.

The meaning of organic farming varies from individual to individual depending on a farmer's economic situation, type of farm, and level of commitment. In its purest form it is an operation that produces, conserves, and recycles all farm needs and inputs. The pure organic farm is a mixed, primarily self-sufficient operation that has livestock, produces crops, and — of course — does not use chemicals. But because of the structure of prairie agriculture, because of its development towards larger, capital-intensive operations and the only recent renewal of organic methods, most organic farms are not self-sufficient. While the level of preservation varies, the main things that bind these farms together are that, first, they do not use chemicals and that, second, they are experimenting or innovating and working towards greater, if not total, self-sufficiency.

It's impossible to know exactly how many organic farmers live on the prairies. In the United States the figure is estimated to be 20,000. In Canada there has been little interest in studying or surveying organic producers and their methods.

At one time in history, though — and it wasn't so long ago — all producers were organic. Prior to the 1940s, agricultural chemicals were not in common use. An estimated 30 pesticides were registered 40 years ago. Today, 405 chemicals form the active ingredient in at least 3,000 name brands. Some farmers who don't as yet refer to themselves as organic seldom use chemicals. They just never got into it. Others have moved away purposefully after sustained use of herbicides, pesticides, fungicides, and synthetic fertilizers.

But there are many producers on the prairies who, while striving towards organic agriculture, do not openly admit it. Organic farmers in Canada are still viewed as oddballs by many of their neighbours. In some communities vocal farmers have been singled out as targets. Some are unable to collect crop insurance or are victims of the Pest Controls Act, which can be used to force farmers to use chemicals if their weed population is deemed too unwieldy or if there is a perceived pest infestation.

As one farmer put it: "We are organic pioneers and someday everybody will know we are right." But, for now, organic producers are often passed off by others in their communities as backwards, poor managers, or left-overs from the 1960s. The peer pressure is tremendous.

Organic farmers seed their land later than chemical farmers because they wait for weeds to appear before planting. Then, tilling the weeds replaces the need to spray them. They also use natural fertilizers such as livestock or green manures — crops grown and ploughed under to return organic matter and nutrients to the soil. Those with livestock do not use growth stimulants or feed additives.

Take Gordon Taylor of Landis, Sask. Almost everything that he grows or produces on his five-quarter farm is recycled. The weeds on the field of summerfallow are mowed naturally by a herd of sheep feeding on them. For the past ten years Gordon has been using the sheep to do partial summerfallow. Later he'll spread their manure back on the land.

To prevent the spread of weed seeds, Gordon collects the chaff that drops behind the combine during harvest. That collection is turned into feed for the animals. His fields are ridged to catch snow and collect moisture for the spring crop. The fences on his farm are made with wire he collected from the telephone company when it transferred its technology underground. You might say he's both an opportunist and a great believer in making do with what you've got — for the sake of protecting and conserving what you've got. In many way he's the archetypal organic farmer, preserving practices that others have neglected and at the same time making "modern" innovations.

Organic farmers go against the mainstream in other ways as well. For instance, they generally farm smaller plots, because they believe it is impossible to care properly for large tracts of land and maintain the diversity and labour necessary for soil replenishment. Each field is different and requires thoughtful cultivation practices. While other farmers move towards specialization and larger equipment and land size, organic farmers believe that trend is the major disrupting force in modern agriculture.

Specialization does not use farm resources or waste-management efficiently, they say. It does not take into account an ecosystem dependent on diversity for sustenance. Without livestock there is no fertilizer. Without cultivated acreage livestock manure becomes a burden. In turn, large equipment means you have to have large fields to manoeuvre through. Farmers who need to pay for expensive equipment through maximum production often plough away windbreaks and waterways or cultivate steep slopes. They may increase production but they also create new erosion problems for themselves, and for others.

Organic farmers have a general principle. Production is necessary but soil and food quality should not be sacrificed. In other words, farmers should not be allowed or — more appropriately — forced by economics to "mine the soil," increasing production by destroying the resource over the long term.

There is plenty of evidence to show that the concept of full production is in practice a matter of mining the soil and turning a renewable resource into a non-renewable one. There are plenty of warning signs pointing to a crisis in agriculture. The environment is a major indicator. Indeed, as a result of public fears about chemical use the organic food industry in supermarkets is estimated to have grown by 20 per cent annually during the last five years. It is a growth that clearly indicates the concern of consumers. Unfortunately for Canadian farmers, 75 per cent of the organic products on Canadian shelves are imported.

While little research has been done in Canada on the possibilities of organic farming, a U.S. Department of Agriculture study states that the alternative is being carried out successfully, even by those who cultivate up to 1,500 acres. The report also states that organic farmers are better managers and more skilful than the average American farmer. A major recommendation in the report is that research and education be increased.

Organic producers are proof that the environment doesn't have to suffer for production. In a farm economy plagued by high interest rates, mounting input costs and low commodity prices, how could organic farmers make it if they were losing nearly a third of their production? Yet in Canada they have received little support for their efforts. In 1981 there were only three scientists in Canada studying soil ecology. Research on biological controls is minimal, although on the increase.

Despite obvious hindrances, organic producers are coming out of the closet. In the mid-1970s a Saskatchewan group called Earthcare helped to publicize ecological agriculture through the publication of scarce information. Those initial steps have gone a long way. In the spring of

86

A natural fertilizer,
near Sonningdale, Saskatchewan

1980 the Ecological Farmers of Manitoba was formed. In July 1983 a group of Saskatchewan farmers, after two years of organizational work, formed the Canadian Organic Producers Marketing Cooperative Ltd. Its numbers doubled in less than a year.

The co-op's objectives include the marketing, pricing, and certification of organic producers. It also wants to develop a quota system for organic products. The co-op is working on a registry of organic producers in an attempt to determine the number of farmers practising ecological agriculture. In time, the co-op hopes to influence the federal government to pass legislation setting out legal standards for organic food.

Those standards will deal with such questions as how many years the soil should be free from agricultural chemicals before its product can be considered organic, and how the products should be handled in the market to maintain their identity. The growers themselves have certification through an affidavit system which states, among other stipulations, that members must not have used chemicals for three years before they market products as organic.

One thing is sure. Organic farmers are conservationists. They do not believe that the environment is infinitely resilient. They differ from a number of urban conservationists in that, while they back the creation of unspoiled parks, they realize that conservation cannot be limited to public reserves. They believe that all of us must co-exist with nature and learn to live with it rather than off of it.

ELMER LAIRD gazes through the picture window from his kitchen table and watches as his neighbour applies anhydrous ammonia by the ton on a patch of land. It's quite the juxtaposition. On Elmer's side of the road the land has not been directly exposed to any commercial chemicals or fertilizers for 14 years.

Elmer is one of the best known organic farmers in Saskatchewan. In 1978 the Davidson-area farmer began a battle to have organic farmers covered under crop insurance. That year Elmer's crop yield was below average and he applied for compensation under the Saskatchewan Crop Insurance Corporation's all-risk crop insurance plan. Adjusters told him his crop failure was due to not using chemicals. Elmer eventually received compensation, although the general treatment of organic farmers was left unresolved.

Later Elmer began to fight a ruling in his municipality that farmers must use pesticides to control grasshoppers. Neither the provincial nor federal departments of agriculture, environment, and health were prepared to agree with Elmer that the municipal bylaw was an infringement on his constitutional rights as an organic farmer whose livelihood and lifestyle depend on growing pure food.

ELMER: I began farming organically in 1969. When I quit using chemicals it was not over a concern for soil or health. At that time I didn't even realize that 2,4-D could have dioxin in it or could be carcinogenic. I quit because we were in an economic slump at that time. The quotas were small and we had piles of wheat all over the farm because the granaries were full. So I cut back on chemicals to save money. The next thing that happened is that I married a librarian and we started digging out information. People were beginning to talk about chemicals and the environment. By the time the markets opened up in 1973, I had sold the sprayer and decided that I wasn't going to use chemicals under any circumstances.

There are a lot of external pressures to use chemicals. Take advertising. I didn't realize until very recently that advertising is convincing top management people in govern-

ment departments that farmers can't farm without chemicals. They really believe it . . . the advertising has gotten to them . . . it's holding them to the chemical route. The myth being promoted is that we're out to feed the hungry world. Well, we aren't feeding the hungry world. We are producing a lot of grain but we aren't even feeding ourselves. Saskatchewan is only producing about 10 per cent of its own vegetables. It could produce 60 per cent.

The only way we are going to feed the world is if we can devise a way to ship commodities to the people who need it rather than to the best-priced markets. Right now, the government and business are arguing about whether we can produce higher yields. On the other hand experts are talking about soil fertility dropping and about millions of acres of saline land. It's just like me entering a mile race when I know I probably can't run from here to the road. We don't know if we have the energy, the fibre, the productivity in the soil to continue producing the amount we already are . . . let alone producing more.

We have to remember that environmental pollution is directly related to health costs. Food ends up in someone's stomach. And it's not just economic costs or health costs. What are you doing to wildlife and the soil? You have to take a holistic view.

Years ago because of a lack of transportation everyone had a milk cow. Because of the stage of development everybody farmed smaller acreages. Now technology, good roads, communications, have changed those factors which preserved the environment. So has government policy. What government policy has done is moved farmers off the land. It has moved their wives off the land into other employment. It has moved farmers themselves into part-time employment. And so rather than grow a bag of carrots, because of time factors, farmers buy the carrots in the grocery store. As a result we don't have people milking cows, people with gardens or root cellars. Farmers are growing crops for export when what we should be doing is feeding ourselves first and exporting the surplus.

I'm not sure what's going to happen. Maybe we're mov-

Elmer Laird,
Davidson, Saskatchewan

ing into an age of psychological breakdown — an age when you can no longer make decisions. We've moved into an age beyond our senses. For example, I had a terrible time getting used to electrical toasters because they were stainless steel and shiny. I'd pick them up because they didn't look hot. Your senses are supposed to protect you. You rely on taste. Is this sweet or sour? You used to pass information on about how to tell when meat was rancid. Now, because we don't produce our own food and we have freezers, people can't tell what's good for them. There may be a bit of poison in everything, but your senses can't tell. All sorts of farmers are saying: "I've sprayed chemicals for 30 years and it hasn't hurt me." But they aren't accepting scientific studies. They accept science on the one hand but not on the other.

As a farmer I think I have a responsibility to produce the most healthy and nutritious food possible and I think I have a responsibility to leave the land in just as good, if not better, state of conservation as I received it in.

The sad thing is that it's only in the last 14 years that I've realized all of these things.

CECIL BURIMA struts around Rockyvale Farm near Blaine Lake, Sask., murmuring in a good-natured baritone about "murder and mayhem on Rockyvale." A weasel has just wiped out half his flock of ducks and Cecil is trying to devise a way to catch the intruder without using chemicals for bait.

Rockyvale is touted as the largest organic farm in Canada — a full seven sections. Cecil isn't prepared to categorize it. He says simply that he hasn't heard of one that is larger. Cecil and his partner, Keith Kennedy — who likes to wear a hat proclaiming "my heart is in farming but my ass is in debt" — cultivate three sections, leaving one in perennial hay and another three in pastureland.

In a sardonic manner, Cecil categorizes himself as a Ukrainian cowboy. His motto is diversification rather than specialization. He has no horses, but does have 165 cows, 2 bulls, 160 chickens, 40 turkeys and a milk cow. Before the weasel invasion he also had 11 ducks.

CECIL: We're as self-sufficient as is possible and practical. We're looking forward to that lovely day when we can do it all ourselves. Right now we are self-sufficient in our own food. Our guiding principle is the well-being and health of the soil. To be involved in producing and not be concerned about the most valuable asset we've got — which is the soil — I think is sinful. We know that as we treat the earth so will we be rewarded.

We have our big sign out by the gate because there's no point in growing pure food unless it's sold as such. We grow 500,000 pounds of grain and 50,000 pounds of rail-grade organic beef every year. We spread 1,000 tons of manure back onto the land. And we know that weeds are just plants that we haven't found a use for...yet.

We also know that the reason we've been able to maintain our farm is because we have lowered our input costs, like fertilizers and chemicals. But we're fighting the odds. The policy of big business, the banking institutes, and the government is to get rid of the extraneous farm population. But this farm comes from nothing and purely because of attitude, fanaticism, and madness it has prospered and has been productive. If the economy collapses we'll still be here... where else is there?

The only way to move away from chemicals is to diversify rather than specialize and that's what we are doing. I feel that it's possible to continue to diversify and intensify our operation. Western Canada has the problem of moisture, but we have two big rivers running through this province that aren't fully utilized. There are thousands of acres in the Outlook area that could be used for the production of vegetables, but aren't because there isn't a market. We are still importing the majority of our food from California and Mexico. As long as that continues it's pointless to diversify and intensify your operation, unless you have a hook.

In our case the hook is "pure food." I think that one of the most important things that can be done in the area of agriculture right now is to increase the awareness of consumers to the point where they demand that the food they eat be pure. And there is no way that anyone can tell me that the food grown in California and Mexico is of a quality that they should be eating.

The critical factor is the consumer. As long as the consumer is willing to settle for food of unpure quality, then agriculture can't really change much.

The price of quality, pure food will come down with demand. One of the problems right now is that pure food is basically a specialty item and is being exploited to a greater and greater extent. If people demand pure food there will also be more people on the land to produce it. We're proud of what we do. We have no doubt about the fact that what we are doing is the right thing to do. That's why the sign is up.

Rockyvale Farm,
Blaine Lake, Saskatchewan

JOHN AND SHIRLEY SARVAS's Rolling Acres Farm near Biggar, Sask., is organic. Everything from the cattlefeed to products for the table is grown without chemical fertilizers or sprays. The cattle and chickens are not given additive supplements, stimulants, or vaccinations. Under the name R.A. Organic Foods, the Sarvas family markets throughout the province.

For the past eight years the Sarvases have also lived a holistic lifestyle. Their term for the health practices they follow is "natural hygiene" and essentially it means removal of white flour, sugar, salt, coffee, tea, alcohol, tobacco, and food additives from the diet. The family believes that they are responsible for the soil, the quality of products they sell, as well as their own health. Not to mention education: Shirley teaches the children at home, using provincially-approved correspondence courses.

John Sarvas takes me out to show me his neighbour's land, seeded that spring, and says it won't bear much fruit. It's basically sand. It has been "chemicalized" to death, says John. His 13-year-old son Mark agrees, pointing to the road that cuts across the eroded field. "You know," Mark says, "you can't even ride your bike on this stuff."

SHIRLEY: Knowledge is what keeps you going. If you understand you can cope. At least you know what's manipulating you.

Finances contribute a lot to the way that farmers are forcing production out of the land. They're pushed so bad economically and the prices on your product keep coming down so you're forced to use practices that if you had a long-term view...a 20 or 30-year view...you wouldn't maybe do your farming that way.

For instance, a farmer may have a thousand or five thousand broilers and the feed company says to him that if he adds arsenic to the feed it sedates the chickens and they'll do better. A small amount of arsenic stimulates the animal's body and it grows faster. So the farmer gets the feed with the arsenic because he needs his animals to produce as much as possible so he can meet his costs. Nobody seems to care, not even the consumer groups.

We realize what is being done to us and we see the situation as extremely hopeless over the long term. You're not going to stay in it forever and you're not going to put your kids back into it because you see what it is. I know guys that are putting their sons in it right today. I wouldn't put my son into agriculture. I can't turn around and put Mark into these hardships.

Urban people want more of everything right now. Rural people sort of go along and they enjoy their touch with agriculture and with the land. But at some point they end up realizing that they are coming up too short.

JOHN: Farmers are always worrying about weeds and getting rid of all their weeds with chemicals. Now, you can't have too many weeds, but the day you don't have any at all, you're in trouble. Weeds don't grow in a desert. Deserts are manmade by mining the soil. I can take you south of here and show you land that, already, weeds won't grow on. He's spreading straw on them, trying to bring the organic matter back into the soil, but that will never come because he has worked that land until there is nothing left but sand. It won't hold water anymore. The thing he has to do now is seed that land down to grass and forget about it for 10 or 15 years to get the organic matter back into it.

You know, if I pour a cup of water onto a sponge there will be very little water that will go around it onto the table. But if I pour a cup of water on that table it runs all over. That's why so much land gets washed off. It won't absorb anymore. We've got to convince farmers that soil is alive. I can take you out to my soil and it has a smell to it. You can smell good soil. But I can take you out to the neighbour who has summerfallowed his land and had chemicals on it for 15 years and it has no texture or smell to it.

Everybody knows what's wrong — university professors, vets, agrologists — but who's going to make waves? You see, I'm the type of person who believes as a humanitarian that you are doing society an injustice if you know something is wrong and you don't say anything or do anything about it…regardless of what it does to your job. You know if we all spoke out you wouldn't have to fear nobody. You could have your job and tell the truth and you'd feel much better. If you don't tell the truth you're not a humanitarian, you are a self-preservationist.

Someday I'll be proved right because organic farming has to come or we are all going to go the way of the dinosaur. We're polluting our land, water, our food, the whole bit. You know very few people die of old age anymore.

Being an organic farmer is one of my problems with the bank. I don't use chemicals, so that's why I'm a poor farmer…that's why I'm an inefficient farmer. That's how they figure it. I believe there are no poor managers with wheat at five dollars a bushel or beef at 70 cents a pound. General Motors and Chrysler or Massey-Ferguson go broke and they can add the cost plus a profit. I can't do that.

We've pondered and pondered. I've pondered over this for 20 years. What is the purpose of all of this? You know, I have a cow and she gets infested with lice. Now those lice don't have any brains and they will infest her and re-infest her until she dies. They'll kill the host. We thought about it often. Why would the banker kill the host? When he's milking you, why should he kill you? How can you have millionaires when there's no one to fleece? You're the one that's laying the golden egg, so why should he want to kill you?

They want control of the land, that's why. You can control people with food. Once they get control they could charge five dollars for an apple and you won't say anything because you have to eat. They'll own the land and we'll rent it or be paid to farm it. But we'll be farming it their way and that won't be ecologically.

John Sarvas,
Biggar, Saskatchewan

BILL BINTNER farms with his brother Richard near Chagoness, Sask. The Bintners were raised in the city and learned to farm through trial and error and with the help of neighbouring farmers. Their farm, Barrier River Bison, has one of the largest buffalo herds in the province.

The Bintner brothers are unusual among the other 60 or so buffalo farmers in Canada in that they don't use antibiotics and growth stimulants common in cattle production. They are committed to a natural form of farming.

When Bill Bintner started farming in the early 1970s it was possible to work off the farm and use the salary to invest in land. It isn't as common today. But the Bintner brothers have also made their operation work by steering away from typical capital-intensive farming, which means growing grain or having a large cattle operation. They are not tied into expensive land inputs or into expensive machinery. Their buffalo run wild during the summer, and for part of the winter forage for willows and grass under the snow in heavily-wooded areas. The major expense on the farm was building miles of eight-foot fence and corrals to hold the buffalo.

BILL: I decided that I didn't want to live in the city and this was a move away from it. Back in the early 1970s I worked in construction and mining and saved my money and invested it in land. I saved up good chunks of money and over a period of four or five years I bought two sections of land. I farm, sandy, rocky, wild areas — marginal arable land. I don't know what would make an urban person want to turn into a rural person. It's just nicer in the country than it is in the city.

We tried organic grain farming in the beginning. It was a learning experience because there was little information on it back in the early 1970s. It was more or less a research project all the time. Mind you, being from the city, every time I turned around and wanted to do some farming I had to research that too. It was just one great big research project, whether it was how to run a combine or how to change the oil in the tractor.

We don't grow much grain anymore. We've been concentrating on our buffalo and growing feed. If you have a climate that is conducive to growing wheat, then I suggest you grow wheat and grow it organically. But if you have a climate that is cold and wet with a short growing season, you're bucking nature by trying to grow wheat. That's why artificial substances and big machinery are used...to get on the land quicker and hope you can beat the season. The fertilizers and sprays are to spur growth.

Now, there's nothing wrong with that except that we are talking about food. The chemicals end up in the grain and if people like those sorts of things — eating chemicals — then that's fine. But you have to ask yourself — and a lot of people are — is this beneficial or is it going to end up causing us problems 20 years down the road?

I have a better chance of surviving at farming by doing it organically and raising buffalo than my neighbours do by growing wheat. The inputs into growing wheat in this area are too high. And I suppose that applies to a lot of other areas as well because the inputs are often higher than what the product you end up with is worth. With buffalo my operating costs are half or a third of what a regular cattle operation runs on.

I think the success of raising buffalo is to keep in mind that they are wild animals and treat them as such. When most people see a buffalo they immediately think of crossing it with a cow. "Beeffalo" is an abomination. People think that the cross will give them the best traits of both. But in fact they end up with something that has the bad traits of both and doesn't make it — a sterile animal. It just doesn't work.

That's the direction of farming: large-scale inefficient operations. The costs of fuel, machinery, and general operating will end up being more and more expensive. That's what's happening in this area. This land was first settled in the 1930s and 1940s. Farmers were just basically living in the bush. On the two sections of land that I own there were nine farmers and this land is mainly all bush. Now it's a much more business-like area — the agribusiness mentality has moved in. They want to open this area up to grow wheat.

There was once a 20-mile forest stretching through here. Most of it has been cut down. The sloughs are being drained, the rivers are being channelled — basically that mentality is revamping the whole area.

I'm into selective clearing, clearing with a purpose in mind and that purpose is leaving some of the diversity. When there is a swamp keep in mind the ducks and the geese and leave the swamp.

Some people call me a bush lover. But there's nothing idle out there. Left alone my land would have lots of timber. That's shelter. Left alone my land would have a deer population of 15 or 20. That's food. I might as well leave a little for the guys that are going to come around in 80 or 100 years. There's no rush to mine it all. Why produce, produce, produce? Canada is self-sufficient in grain so maybe we should ease off on that and think about our natural resources and what we are doing. All we're doing now is mining the soil. I think we're shortsighted.

My goal is to have a self-sufficient operation, one that is ecologically sound. I don't see getting larger as an option. I don't see the reasoning behind that. All that happens when you get larger is that you increase the stakes. It's a gamble. It gets to the point that when you do make a mistake you can't cover your problems. And you're going to lose. You're going to lose the whole operation and there goes another farmer.

Bill Bintner,
Chagoness, Saskatchewan

96

AL SHERESKY shows me his flour and the mills he uses for grinding. He is obviously proud of the organic products he produces on his one-section farm near Glen Ewen, Sask. He is also keen to see that someone from "outside" is interested in his operation. The stacks of flour warehoused on his farm will end up on shelves across Canada.

Right now, Al is trying to find a good price on cotton bags to replace the plastic weave he has been using to package the flour. There are people, he says, who can't eat anything that has been touched by plastic because they suffer from an environmental illness. Perhaps too, a good cotton bag can be recycled into dish cloths or blouses.

Al has been farming "more or less" organically for 30 years. But in the last seven, he says, he has become very disciplined. The label attached to each bag of flour says it all: "This product has been produced, processed and packaged without the use of any chemical fertilizers, herbicides, pesticides or preservatives. It is a natural, pure, wholesome and poison free food."

AL: When chemicals were just coming out you would read these full-page ads that said increase your profit by three dollars an acre. My father just ate that up — most people did. Now in the textbooks they write that they are not sure what the effects of chemicals are. A few years ago there was not even this hint of concern.

We have to do something. We can't just go on. All we need is just one or two years of no rain — the whole place would just blow. Everything depends on the life of the soil. The farmer is very dependent on favourable weather. I'm getting 25 or 30 bushels of wheat an acre and I don't think chemical farmers in this area are getting much more and they have the cost of all of those inputs.

But most people are not satisfied with just an average crop. They push that soil to the hilt. Many want the very most they can obtain. What for? It's a short-term project. Sure we'll get it, but we'll pay for it in the end. Now some of the older farmers are saying: "Hey, that organic farming is what we used to do." And they're trying it again.

I work like a dog, but I like to do it. I don't care to have a new car or a new tractor every year. What's it all about? Helping your fellow man, right? We're not here to make a million. We're here to make a living and do some good for somebody. I don't want to be a good little consumer.

I quit all poisons seven years ago when I started developing a market for organic food. What I would like to see is a modified type of organic farming. If people used proper cultivation practices most farmers could cut their inputs by 80 per cent. But now, the way it is, you turn on the radio and you hear: "It'll pay you, it'll pay you. Put this on cause you've got a weed." They want you to kill every last weed. But weeds have benefits. People think a weed is a weed — get rid of it. It's the same with an insect — get rid of it. But when you get rid of it you get rid of 100 others that are good. You know, there was a farmer in here the other day and I said to him that while there were a lot of grasshoppers I'd noticed a lot of black crickets around too. Did he know that crickets ate grasshopper eggs? No, he didn't, so he'd been kicking them out of his way. People aren't in touch with nature anymore.

The farms are getting too big. I don't like these massive sections. We are not really more efficient farmers. We're efficient with labour, but that's it. It's the little farmer who is more efficient. He uses every scrap. A semi-truck went past here the other day and spilled a whole bunch of fertilizer and it was just left. That wasn't a small farmer. I can take you out to the fields and show you bald spots left in the field from where the chemical farmer started his nitrogen machine or sprayer. He killed everything on that spot for years.

The more land the farmer has or the more in debt he becomes, the more impatient he is. People would be better to have two small combines and pay a person to run one rather than have one big expensive combine. It would help the machinery dealer and employment too.

But instead we're headed towards more control. The fewer farmers there are the easier the control because once you control the food supply you can turn governments over and you can do whatever you want. Farmers don't think they are being told what to do — but they are.

Al Sheresky,
Glen Ewen, Saskatchewan

ALFRED MOORE keeps pigs on his one and a half section farm near Dinsmore, Sask. But Alfred hates pigs. They get into the garden and eat the vegetables. They break their pens and run across the road and it seems like a never-ending chase to get the pigs under control.

But Alfred also believes that to be an organic producer means using and recycling waste on your farm. The pigs eat the screenings from his grain. The manure can be used on the land. And the pigs are pork for the table. Along with the 25 head of cattle that he keeps, it's all part of good management.

Three or four years ago anyone would have been hard-pressed to find more than a handful of self-proclaimed organic producers. It was anathema to admit to the practice in a rural community. Times are changing. On July 19, 1983, after two years of organizing, 26 producers founded the Canadian Organic Marketing Producers Co-Op Ltd. Six months later membership had doubled and it continues to grow. Alfred Moore is the chairman of the Co-Op.

ALFRED: My father was one of the first in the community to have a sprayer. But when a member of your family dies of cancer you begin to wonder. My mother died of cancer in 1970. I guess those kinds of concerns led me to organic farming. When I started six years ago I hoped organic farming was possible. I wasn't as convinced then as I am now. I'm darn sure it's possible now.

You start thinking . . . is it worth the two or three extra bushels an acre when you are poisoning people? And in the long run I think there will be a dollar or two more in organic farming than there is in commercial farming. I think money will change a lot of people over eventually. A lot of farmers are talking about the high cost of chemicals and they're wondering what to do about it.

I really believe that people shouldn't have to pay more for quality food. I believe in the long run that we should have nothing but quality food. There should really be only one standard. Given today's double standard, though, there is more work in producing organic food. More effort goes into

keeping it separate to maintain its identity. If we only had one standard for food our present system of getting food to consumers would be more than adequate.

As the word gets out it becomes easier for the guy who has been farming without chemicals for 10 or 12 years to admit that he is an organic producer. You know when you're the only one in the community who's not spraying and you're a week or so later in seeding than the rest of them, they start looking and saying, "I wonder what that lazy so and so is doing — he's not out here with the rest of us." They look at you as something strange. The peer pressure that comes from doing it is probably the hardest thing. As far as doing it, you just have to make up your mind and go through the steps. But a lot of people are watching — all of your neighbours are watching — almost waiting for you to fail. The proof is in the pudding. Now there's not as many snide remarks as there used to be.

Organic producers need an ecological department of agriculture because we are entitled to the research and the extension services that we need. There needs to be legislation to certify or spell out what an organic producer is. If you go into a health-food store you think that all the foods are organic, and while they may all be, each person has a different standard or definition of what organic means. The Co-Op has certification standards for its members so we can say this is exactly what we sell.

Twenty-section farms are much more difficult to manage organically than two-section farms. We are going to have to start looking at farm size and all of those questions. But I don't believe in going back to horses.

My definition of efficiency is to get the job done with the highest quality, with the least cost and effort and still have time to live. The system defines efficiency as larger and bigger and more capital-intensive. I think you should produce as much as you can produce. I'd like to produce two blades of grass where before there was only one, but not artificially. The philosophy is different.

Alfred Moore,
Dinsmore, Saskatchewan

DANE WRIGHT lives on a section of land near Spiritwood in northern Saskatchewan. His land is marginal and is off in the bush. Simply follow the road as far as it will go: "That'll be our farm," says Dane. Since the early 1970s Dane has lived on this land, but he doesn't categorize himself as a farmer. "I'm an Orgnik." I take that to mean he is an organic beatnik.

At one point a number of people lived on this farm in communal style. All of them are gone now. The visions of living off the land just didn't pan out. But Dane and his family show no signs of leaving.

It's the ninth crop, according to Dane. For a few years they didn't seed more than a garden. At any given time no more than 110 acres have been seeded to wheat, oats, and barley. Dane is not producing for the market but only to satisfy his family's food needs. He inherited his land and is not tied into the agri-system or the financial structure.

The Wrights live in an old school house, without running water. A number of farm buildings are made of logs, mud, and sticks. During the summer food is collected as needed, sometimes from the garden and sometimes from the bush.

DANE: We live simply but we do not want for too much. It's only in the last year that I've accepted a light bulb. Sometimes you realize that things can be carried too far. You have to try to live with nature without being too destructive. Still, the kids like to watch "Sesame Street" and the program is pretty good . . . so . . .

If the money goes to hell in a bucket we are not badly situated. We have a root cellar for the essentials — for the meat and potatoes of life. We have enough grain for our own needs to last two years.

The diversity in our fields is phenomenal. Look, here we have camomile for tea, as well as wild mint. These are all wild plants that we can harvest for our own needs.

I cultivate small fields to assess the kinds of crops that are best grown. We don't want to perform experiments on such a grand scale as chemists would have us do with the whole of agriculture. The type of farming I do is biological transmutation.

When agrologists say that we have lost 50 per cent of the nitrogen in the soil, their view of the soil is that it is a non-renewable resource. With no religious overtones — the man in the Garden of Eden could build the soil by participation.

Slow is fast. It's an old Zen proverb and it's true. That's what's necessary when it comes to agriculture.

Dane, Susan, Carmen, and Diana Wright,
Spiritwood, Saskatchewan

ED GILLIS began limiting his use of farm chemicals over ten years ago, when he discovered that his health demanded pure food. He found that he could not condone producing contaminated food for others when it was not fit for his own consumption. With wife Marilyn and two children, the Gillis family farms three quarters near Wynyard, Sask.

ED: I'm running into more and more people — farmers — who are questioning chemical use. Some farmers know they shouldn't be using chemicals but they hesitate and are for some reason frightened to break away from the chemicals. I guess maybe they're just a little scared that it won't work, you know. I think we're all that way sometimes...when it comes to changing jobs you hesitate, just in case it doesn't work, you know.

A lot of people are chained in or tied to these chemicals because of the importance of producing more all the time. Farmers are forced into it because of the high costs of all of the inputs. You either have to get more land or more production or both.

Since I don't use fertilizers and weed-sprays I don't have the expenses so I don't have to produce as much. I like to see quality food. I think if we put more emphasis on quality rather than quantity we'll achieve better results in the long run and have healthier people too.

Efficiency means producing more with less inputs, less work, and less expense. That could be one way of being efficient. That's where the chemical companies have us. They are trying to convince us that we are producing more with less. I certainly think that can be questioned.

Prices are a big problem. I think we are being forced into a type of farming that we don't really want. Also I think we are being forced into a lifestyle that we don't really want. We, and most farmers, don't want to work 12 and 15 and maybe 18 hours a day. I sometimes think we have a real tiger by the tail with these chemicals. Using chemicals encourages people to expand their operation. We just don't know what we're doing and what the end result is going to be.

But have we a choice when it comes to deciding about organic farming? This is the way that I'd put it — have we a choice? I don't think we have much choice except to go away from chemicals, and the only way I think is to go into organic farming. Otherwise we may end up with land that resembles something like the moon and can't be used for much more than a reflecting surface for the sun's rays.

Ed Gillis,
Wynyard, Saskatchewan

104

GERARD AND ARLETTE GAUDET have logged more than a decade as farmers near the northern Saskatchewan French community of Bellevue, turning to organic farming a few years back. They've had setbacks but intend to continue farming organically on a small scale. About all they can risk seeding at this point is 40 acres, considering that they are locked into a 19 per cent loan with no money to pay the penalty to renegotiate.

The Gaudets satisfy most of their own food needs through their farm. They produce milk, butter, bread, beef, and vegetables, and the family estimates that their efforts are the equivalent of a $4,000 to $5,000 food bill from the local grocery check-out counter. The personal expenses for their family of six were about $4,000 in 1982. That was also their net income.

ARLETTE: What we like about farming is the lifestyle. You can do your own thing. You can grow your own garden. You can have the influence of close neighbours on your children and your own influence as parents is much more dominant than in the city. We like living with the land — living with life.

I think the biggest concern of it all is having children... respect for life. Here you can teach your children to appreciate the simplest thing...the life in the soil...the life in the slough...and if you can instill in them the respect for this kind of life they will respect any other life. That's why to us losing the farm is more than losing the house or the land. We only care for those things because we care for this environment.

GERARD: We're not farming for the money. We'd like to survive and be happy doing it. We want to be successful enough to feed and clothe our children and be happy doing it. Our financial situation was terrible until this month when we sold the one quarter. Before that we were losing everything. Every morning we'd get up and even before opening our eyes the bank would take 53 dollars in interest. You'd owe that much more every day, and all we owned was three quarters.

We couldn't make payments with the high interest rates,

so there was interest on interest. The reason for that was two crop failures, which we are not to blame for and the banks are not to blame for. Now that we've sold that quarter we're better off but we still have a lot of debt and if we have another crop failure this fall we'll have to sell another quarter next spring.

We started organic farming four years ago and this is the first year the product would have been considered organic. But we had to sell that quarter of land. It was the only parcel that had no buildings on it.

ARLETTE: We have this philosophy, this idea, that only life supports life. You can chew on a rock all you like and get minerals but it's still dead stuff. By feeding the soil life through green manures and the like you produce a very healthy plant and if you eat it that will keep you healthy and make you more resistant to disease and sickness. We feel that most people are sick because they are overfed and undernourished. We thought that maybe we should practise what we thought by farming organically.

GERARD: But we started organic farming at a bad time. We had debts to pay and by the time we'd made the transition to organic growing we were too much in debt. While we were making the conversion our yields were cut and we were getting a regular price — not the price for organic products. So the income from the land was almost cut in half. After three years, when we could have sold the wheat as organic, we were too much in debt and had to sell that quarter. And we actually had two years of rain and one of frost.

But we haven't abandoned it. Right now we still have 40 acres of alfalfa and when we plough it down it will be organic. Then we'll begin with another 40 acres. We'd feel like traitors to ourselves if we stopped. We think it is the right and proper way to feed people.

ARLETTE: We think people are not paying enough for their food. This country's cheap food policy is just the pits. Everybody thinks the farmers are getting the money, but it just

Arlette and Gerard Gaudet,
Bellevue, Saskatchewan

isn't true. We have cream and if we sold it to the creamery we would get three dollars a quart. With one quart of cream you cannot make a pound of butter, but people are buying butter at the store for two dollars and 15 cents a pound. I don't get it. Because there's more than three dollars worth of cream in there, plus the labour. Who's subsidizing that pound of butter? We were making butter to sell but if I paid myself three dollars an hour I'd have to sell that pound for four dollars and 50 cents. We have cattle and we're not making a penny. It costs us 450 dollars a year to feed a cow and you have to keep that cow two years and then sell it for 900 or 1,000 dollars. Basically we're working for the Red Cross.

You know, a few years ago when we were talking to an urban relative about the financial problems we were having he said to us: "Well, why don't you just sell it? That's better than we can do." Well, what can you say? It's true, but you have to understand the love that a person has for the land and the life. Others maybe don't want to be on the farm. We do. If we weren't here who would be? They believe what Trudeau has said about farmers — that we are just a bunch of complainers.

GERARD: You know, they say you're asset rich and cash poor. Well that's true, but we're getting asset poor too.

BILL OLSON   If you travel west on Highway 3, just past Pierson, Man. and almost into Saskatchewan, you come to Bill and Lois Olson's "Organic Acres." Bill says that his five-quarter farm has never completely supported his family of ten children. It's been subsidized with off-farm labour from teaching as well as other odd jobs. But he says it has provided his children with pure organic food, which he, in part, credits for his kids' intelligence and ambition. Lois, on the other hand, credits the organic food for Bill's bragging.

Out in the barn, Bill shows me his goats. Goat's milk, he says, is the best thing for ulcers because its base is more alkaline than cow's milk. Rather than weeding out goats according to milk production, Bill chooses to keep those that can be tamed — tamed meaning those that can handle human affection.

While Bill loves animals and argues that love and care produce lots of piglets, when it comes to the soil it is "humosity" that nurtures it. "Humosity" is a term that Bill has coined by combining the two most important traits of soil: humus and porosity.

BILL: The last time we tried to poison ourselves was 1956. It's frustrating when you know how things should be done but they aren't. Farming organically is fairly simple. Number one, you have to start farming in co-operation with nature. Timing is very important. If you're out of time you're basically working for the weeds. An ordinary farmer has to watch the things around him. You have to watch nature where it has not been disturbed by man.

Man shouldn't grumble when his weird attempts at changing nature fail. It's his own fault for trying to control a force bigger than himself.

Some people think that organic farming means going backwards. But in fact you need the latest equipment to do it so that you can get on the land at the right time and move quickly to overcome the weed problems. Unfortunately, a young person who's been using chemicals cannot just quit farming chemically. He has to start with one field until he has the experience and has built the soil bit by bit. I strongly recommend a crash program of kicking it out the window. But you can't do that. You'd starve. So you have to start slowly until you know what you're doing and your soil is in balance naturally.

I know some farmers who get brainwashed by the happy-hour sales tactics of the chemical companies. One farmer was going to market his organic grain for 12 dollars a bushel. He was almost convinced to go organic. But instead he went to a chemical meeting. He decided to turn down 12 dollars a bushel and came home with a new coat and a new cap.

Sometimes things can really startle you. You know, we've had hog raisers coming here to buy pigs. One asked me how much I wanted. I said ten cents over market price per pound. He said that was fine. So I said, back your truck up and we'll load her up. "Oh no," he said, "I'll slaughter it right here." The conditions weren't very sanitary, but he was satisfied. You see, he didn't care who was eating his product. He just cared about the profit he made on his pigs — but he wouldn't eat them himself.

Bill and Lois Olson,
Pierson, Manitoba

GORDON TAYLOR, like most farmers, is innovative. But on his five-quarter farm near Landis, Sask., he has added a few new twists to organic farming.

His 40-acre fields are smaller than usual and divided by miles of windbreaks planted several years ago. Small fields mean that smaller equipment is needed to manoeuvre within them, but Gordon believes that is the only way to prevent the coming of another dustbowl. He admits that his system of farming is not foolproof, but he's satisfied with the results and the level of conservation. As he puts it, "People say, 'What's that damn fool doing now?'. You have to be fairly thick-skinned."

Although his methods are unorthodox, Gordon is participating in a program on energy efficiency sponsored by the Saskatchewan Research Council. His practices are obviously not to be discounted.

GORDON: I've been an organic farmer since I started farming in 1951. I don't know why I took this route, I guess I'm a nonconformist. I went to the Agriculture Rep in 1955. There was some land for sale and he said, "Buy it, buy it." But, I thought, why? If I'm going to go broke I might as well go broke with what I have. I could see what was happening. We were losing farmers and people and it just didn't go down well. The organic route was what I felt in my heart was the way we should go. And I've been advocating we should have limits to land size since about that time. But people would tell me I should go to Russia. Now a lot of groups are advocating it, so maybe it isn't all that bad an idea, eh!

Money is such a by-product. There's no substitute for it but if I based success on money I'd really have missed the boat. If I have to drive a Versatile four-wheel-drive tractor, well.... I've only had two new implements in my life. Most of my trucks are old enough to vote. I'm trying not to be a slave to the economic system.

Sure, our productivity has really increased over the years. So I get out the pencil and paper and I figure. These guys that are doing all this intensive farming with chemicals, they're getting maybe 30 bushels to the acre but it takes 15 bush-

els to the acre just to pay their expenses. I get 22 and it may take 10 to pay my expenses. So how much better off are they than I am? Who are they working for? Maybe they're working for the guys who are supplying the goods and services, the chemicals. At least what I get is mine. Maybe the yields aren't as good and maybe there are some weeds in it, but maybe I can go away to the lake for a day or two and not be racked by stress because I didn't get my spraying done.

Then there is the social aspect of it. Who controls the land and how? I think the land-banking system of owning land is the only way of owning it. As far as I'm concerned I shouldn't have title to this land. All I am is a steward of it while I'm here. You know the way we've been doing it is we've had a perpetual mortgage. If I want to retire in dignity I have to burden my kids with a debt by selling them the land so I can retire, because my pension plan is tied up in this land. And the only people that are making money are those who transfer titles and those who lend the money.

If I had tenure of this land until I was 55 I could put money aside instead of paying for it and I'd have a pension and then the land could be turned over to whoever wanted to farm it without burdening them with a debt that they have no way of ever paying for. Then you wouldn't have to mine the soil and create deserts to pay for the land.

If we ever get a sustained wind one of these years our land is going to all be down in the Gulf of Mexico. It's just going to blow away.

You can see the concentration of land. I think what's going to happen is that the banks will be owning the land eventually. We are going to have tenant farmers. When we get food production in the control of corporations, they're not going to do things that are good for the land. They'll do what's good for the bottom line. We have to think about quality food. If conglomerates control, what kind of product will consumers get? Who wants to eat a tomato that can fall 40 feet without bruising?

Urban people think farmers are rich because they have land, equipment, and maybe even a four-wheel-drive tractor. But the farmer doesn't own the door handle on any of them.

Gordon Taylor,
Landis, Saskatchewan

CHAPTER SIX CO-OPERATIVE FARMING: THE MAVERICKS

THE MAVERICKS

"Why should farmers own the land? Fishermen don't own the seas." I turn the farmer's words over and over in my mind, analyzing their wisdom and knowing full well that these words are heresy to the average prairie farmer.

The concept of co-operative farming has its source in that type of wisdom, although the organization, its functions, and goals are different on every co-op farm. Some co-op farmers live on individual farmsteads, or in the same house, or in the same yard with houses grouped together. But the basis of the co-operative farm remains the same: sharing and democracy. What is shared varies according to each group, but major decisions are made democratically: one member, one vote and the majority rules.

In Saskatchewan, the home of the co-operative farm movement, there are currently 55 farm production co-ops, which can be categorized into three groups. One is the machinery co-op in which farmers retain ownership of their land but share machinery and labour, and pool the sales of their produce according to the percentage of acreage each farmer owns. The second is the agri-pool in which farmers retain individual ownership of land but rent it to the co-op. The co-op owns the machinery, pays wages for labour, and the co-op's surplus income is divided among the producers.

The third type, and no doubt the most ambitious, is the full co-op. This co-op owns the land, machinery, and buildings, and pays each member a wage, with net income either being divided among its members or put back into the operation.

In the early 1940s the Saskatchewan government, then led by the Co-operative Commonwealth Confederation (CCF), made a concerted effort to establish official farm co-ops. The move towards mechanization, the inherent costs to individual farmers, the increased production necessary for the war effort, and later the return of veterans created a situation in which co-operative farming made economic sense. During that decade hopes were high for the establishment of co-ops and, from 1946 to 1949, 16 co-op farms were formed in Saskatchewan. To this day the province has a Department of Co-operatives.

Still, farming co-operatively has never been very popular on the prairies, at least not in an official, structured way. One of the main reasons is that many farmers think that collective work gobbles up identity, the power to make decisions, the work ethic, and personal pride.

But all of the co-op farms I visited exuded a strong sense of satisfaction and achievement, in some cases moreso than most family operations. Working as part of a group on a daily basis means having more people around to solve tough problems and to handle big jobs — decreasing some of the personal tensions that come from working in isolation or with only a few family members to help. It also means a farmer can take a holiday even if there is livestock or poultry around to feed, and on the whole it means the farmer is not left alone to deal with severe bouts of penury. Most co-op farmers don't wear the same clothes or hold the same ideas. But they do share one trait. They know that collective work is a form of mutual protection.

By sharing equipment and labour and buying necessary inputs in bulk they lower the costs of running the farm. They cut down on the number of necessary repair shops and tools and the need for large machinery. They are also finding out that agriculture eats up less land when it is done co-operatively. While co-op farmers may pool their land and end up working very large farms — sometimes 10 or 20 sections — they still can't be considered "large" or "corporate" farmers if the numbers of people supported by the farm are divided into the land base. Farming co-

Lakeside Co-op meeting,
Dafoe, Saskatchewan

operatively generally takes less land than individual farms to support the same number of people.

About half of the co-ops in Saskatchewan have been formed within families. What often happens is that parents, sons, and daughters who have worked together unofficially for years decide to legalize the arrangement and establish a co-operative. The Ardoch co-op farm is one example. In other cases neighbours decide to get together. But generally, no matter whether a co-op is formed within a family or not, the same rule applies: the more people involved, the more opportunities exist. Often, for instance, co-op farmers can set up group insurance plans, disability programs, and pension funds. An individual farmer within a co-op, if injured or aged, doesn't necessarily have to sell land off to the highest bidder to ensure an adequate income for the rest of his or her life.

In addition it becomes more practical to care properly for large gardens or greenhouses if more labour is available. On the Matador Co-op Farm, members equipped with various ideas or skills are able to build their own homes and farm buildings or repair equipment while fellow members carry on with other tasks. One person may like to do bookwork, while another may want to care for livestock or do the seeding. For instance, the original Matador farm had its own grocery store and, for a time, a school. The group decides what it needs to survive and prosper and what it can afford.

Many co-ops also find that it takes less labour per individual to do the work than on most ordinary farms. For example, for all farms the most crucial times of year are seeding and harvest. On the Matador farm, instead of having one person ride the machinery for hours, trying to beat the clock and the weather while someone else, usually a wife, keeps busy preparing and bringing meals to the field, the co-op uses eight-hour shifts and operates machinery overtime for long stretches if necessary — without it being a drain on one person. One or two people make meals, others do the washing up, while still others carry food and drink out to the field. Working together, once again, less-

ens the load and the stress for each person.

That's not to say that co-operative farming runs smoothly at all times. On many co-ops members have to face an often unwelcome routine of regular meetings and the inherent problems created by group dynamics. Democracy can be a lengthy process and each person has to be prepared to voice an opinion (and listen to others' opinions) and wait out a group decision. A more unfortunate fact is that on most existing co-ops women are excluded from membership because a brand of traditional thinking — the "woman's place" sort of thing — tends to predominate. There are, however, co-ops where women are active members and anything from gardening to day care to working the machines is possible and worthy of a wage.

Another problem is that while co-op farming is an outgrowth of economic necessity, in the past income tax laws favoured incorporation as opposed to co-operation. In many cases, government loan programs or commodity assurance programs do not recognize the full number of members. In yet other cases, while individual family farmers are able to roll over their land to the next generation at reduced tax rates, co-operatives are categorized as corporate farms and many must pay capital gains even if the property is transferred to family.

The Matador Co-op Farm is once again one of the best examples of the pitfalls awaiting co-ops that succeed. It was established on Aug. 20, 1946, near Kyle, Sask., when 17 people formed the organization under the Veteran's Land Act, aimed at establishing returning soldiers on the farm. By 1974 the Matador had proved that working and living together were manageable and rewarding ways of farming. Although members had come and gone over the previous 28 years, five of the original farmers remained. Most of them were reaching retirement age and the task before them was to overcome the difficulties of transferring the land to the second generation, at a time when high land values were leading some of the members into thinking about selling to the highest bidder. Other members wanted, however, to turn over the land to sons and daughters without saddling them with a huge debt. But coming up with the money to turn the land over to a collective was a problem. Traditional loan companies frown on lending large sums for land that will be communally operated.

Eventually, internal disputes were overcome and the co-op was sold to the Saskatchewan government under the Land Bank program. It was then rented to the second generation. The Matador Farming Pool, made up of 11 members, seems likely to survive for at least a generation, just as the Matador Co-op farm did.

While some co-op problems could be dealt with through improved federal legislation, others cannot. For instance, while co-op farms are formed to lower the costs of farming and often to create the opportunity for a second generation of farmers, external factors such as speculation and inflation of land prices often create a bind, making it difficult for young people to form a co-op farm. On established farms the value of the farm increases with time, making it difficult for new members to buy in. Long-term members may want to leave the co-op and be paid market value for their share. These factors can severely curtail the life expectancy of a co-op farm by either reducing cash flow or forcing the sale of property. As in the Matador case, if members decide to prohibit the sale or removal of land from the co-op, they find they are creating problems for themselves by limiting the credit available from private financial agencies. Communal land is not the banks' idea of security.

The only way to deal with speculation, inflation, and the coming and going of members was once explained to me as the "shirt sleeves co-op." It doesn't exist yet, but basically the concept is that members join with personal belongings and if they decide to quit farming that is what they leave with. The land and capital would be publicly owned with co-op members having land tenure.

But putting aside the intricacies of co-op farms, it is clear that they can support many more people, increase productivity without increasing land base, lessen the work load and diversify an operation much easier than a family farm can. Co-operative farms tend to emphasize conserva-

tion over expansion, and sharing over competition. This lessens the need for large and numerous pieces of equipment and for heavy capital investment — and the resulting need to borrow at high interest rates. For government and business, that kind of emphasis means a reduction in the possibilities for making flashy gains — for profiteering — from farmers and the land.

LORNE DIETRICK, one of the original members of the Matador Co-op, still lives on the farm, a small community near Kyle, Sask., that technically — with its 40 residents — qualifies as a hamlet. When you first enter the farm you see 14 houses forming a large crescent, and at the centre a park area and community hall. The wooden shingles and peeling paint on the hall indicate this is not a new enterprise.

The farm itself covers 13 sections, yet if divided by the numbers of farmers working on it, is smaller than the average prairie farm. It is the oldest existing co-op on the prairies and one of the first formed in Saskatchewan. In its open park area in July 1947, 3,000 people gathered to celebrate the first anniversary of the Matador experiment. Today it is still an exciting place, challenging the individualistic view of farming and providing an example of sustainable economics and efficiency.

LORNE: In 1946, after the war, you couldn't buy a tractor. All of our factories had been utilized to produce war equipment and there was a great shortage of farm machinery. As a result it was very necessary to take advantage of the few machines that were available and a group could do that better than an individual. Seventeen of us pooled our resources and we were able to buy three tractors from war assets, and these tractors were our main source of power. For vehicles, we had two jeeps and four army trucks.

We've been successful in the way that we've continued to operate and we've managed to transfer the farm to the next generation. In that regard I consider we've been very successful because a good many family farms today fail to pass on their farm to the next generation.

What's success? What's the criteria? Is it accumulating a lot of money and becoming wealthy? Is it how you look after the land? Is it how you develop a resource? What's the yardstick? Now, some co-ops have been very successful in the way that they have made lots of money and had good retirement pension funds. But many of them failed because they didn't pass the land on to the next generation as a co-operative.

I would hope that eventually co-operatives will be used to repopulate rural Saskatchewan. Co-operative farming should be the basis to re-establish people back into agriculture rather than have them competing with one another. I think this farm is a good example of the use of technology and labour to create efficiency and a high standard of living.

But unless there is a sympathetic government, proper legislation, and the right kind of land tenure program, it won't happen. Today we do not have adequate land tenure programs or proper tax legislation or proper encouragement on the part of governments for people to go into groups and co-op farms.

A proper land tenure program should be a long-term use-lease system of land holding, which means that land would be used as a resource rather than a commodity. You would lease land at a rate that would not be revenue-bearing for the government but would be in the interest of seeing that those people who were using the land were building the soil as well as producing grains or product from it. I think one of the things that we could do with a long-term use program is revitalize and rebuild our soils, which is really needed. If we continue on the way we are, where land is recapitalized every generation, it's the land that is going to suffer. Paying for the land every generation doesn't meet the needs of the soil or aid in transferring it to the next generation.

As long as land is a commodity we'll have difficulty. The capital to pay for the land has got to come from production of the land and, therefore, you mine the land, rather than build it. Every time you have to pay for that land, that payment has to come out of production. If you had a long-term program of land tenure you wouldn't have to refinance the land every time it changes hands, and farming would carry on from generation to generation.

The Land Bank program in Saskatchewan was the only method that we could use to transfer this farm to the next generation. Now there are of course shortfalls in the Land Bank leasing program, especially for a co-operative. I think there should be no right of purchase in a Land Bank lease to a co-operative. In our case, though, there is some protection because 90 per cent of the membership must be in fa-

Lorne Dietrick and Matador swathing crew,
Kyle, Saskatchewan

vour of purchase. The lease, of course, is in perpetuity with the right of transfer to the next of kin.

117

Another thing is that farm size is not spelled out. I think it should be in a co-operative farm's interest to see how many people can be involved in a given farm operation, rather than see how many acres can be made available to a group of people. I think we must have the land base related to the population base. We started on a three-quarter section of land and every time an additional three-quarters of land was brought in we required another member. On the Matador the land lease program established that there must be 11 members on this land base.

Co-op farms can be the instrument to repopulate the rural areas. The corporate farm will depopulate, that's for sure, because the corporate farm eliminates people for profit. The co-operative farm depends on intensification and people for profit. There isn't much difference between the corporate and co-operative farms other than philosophy. They can both farm a large area of land. They can both utilize science and technology much better than the family farm. But the corporate does it for the manager or single owner, whereas the co-operative has to base itself on a social concept. That's the difference. It also has to organize itself democratically and make decisions in that way.

Corporate farms may hire large numbers of farm labourers but that won't bring harmony. If that kind of development continues to take place, farm labour will have to unionize and fight the bosses to protect themselves. Whereas if you form a co-operative you bring in democracy and you try to divide up the income, labour, and leisure time equitably among the people who participate. The corporate owner has the sole power to determine how he distributes the earnings and the hours of labour and leisure. That's the difference.

Our governments have not been supportive of co-operative farms. They tolerate them, that's all. The provincial government, in the beginning the CCF, passed legislation and were behind the co-operative movement for about four or five years. But after that they saw that it wasn't going to be a good political move, so they cooled off on it and didn't put up the fight that was necessary. And you can't put all the blame on government. Some of our co-operative farms had difficulty making decisions and working together. People said it wouldn't work and this had an effect upon the government.

There's no source of capital available to buy a co-op. You can't get a loan through the Farm Credit Corporation. The provincial government has no source available unless the co-op sells its land to the Land Bank. Traditional lending facilities won't lend for co-operatives because if you have by-laws which preclude the sale of the land they never see themselves being able to regain their security. Those institutions are not interested in making common property out of land. Philosophically they don't fit in. Therefore, the philosophy has to be developed by government agencies and those interested in programs that would build communities.

I think if nothing is done the corporate farm will eventually be the dominant force in agriculture. If we just leave the contending forces to battle for the utilization of land and technology, then without question, it won't have to be foreign capital or some big corporate entity that will come in. Within the farm community today there are those people who will become the corporate farmers. They have managerial skills and backing, no social conscience, and they are only concerned about acquiring property and wealth. And there's enough of that among farmers today to find enough people in that kind of mental frame to establish corporate farms. They won't be imported. They're home-grown.

Governments can talk all about their interest in family farming. They can talk about their desire to see the family farm as the basis of agriculture, but unless they do things like limit farm size, create a new land tenure system, encourage co-ops, it's all just talk.

By and large there is not enough commitment on the part of family farmers to protect themselves. They're not organized. Each farmer is the other's competitor. Each one is waiting until the next one dies so that he can get the land.

It's happening very rapidly now. At one time you would absorb one half-section to enlarge your farm, but now the two-section farmer is absorbing the two-section farmer. It's

gaining momentum. It could happen in this generation or in 10 or 15 years. The end of the Crow Rate will make it much faster. If the Canadian Wheat Board goes it will really go quick. These have been the last controls on the corporate. The Wheat Board has a quota system delivery which inhibits the big fella and the freight rate system made it possible for the small farmer to have low, secure rates. When these things are taken away corporations will grow fast.

Matador Farm members: two generations,
Kyle, Saskatchewan

Dale Stewart This year is the tenth anniversary of the Matador Farming Pool. Its 11 members, all under 35, are busy building new homes of their own. They are obviously proud of the changes the new Matador is undertaking. While some of the members are the children of original members, Dale Stewart was not raised on the Matador. He applied to join when the co-op was being transferred to the second generation. The existence of the co-op has provided him with an opportunity he doubts would have surfaced otherwise.

Dale: I wasn't brought up on a farm, but I've always been interested in farming. I don't know if I'd have put a co-op farm as a priority over an individual farm, I was just interested in farming. The cost of getting into farming, and not being the son of a farmer, meant that other options just weren't available.

We all put money into the co-op, but the difference was that we were able to set up through the Land Bank and not pay huge land payments. Plus, with 11 members together we could set up things cheaper. The goal of the co-op is to maintain the co-op farm as a way of life and business for all of its members. It would be nice to maintain it for a third generation. I hope the majority of members want to maintain it in perpetuity.

As inflation takes its toll and everything goes up, I don't think our members would mind increasing our land base. The average land base per unit in the province is 960 acres and we are under that. I don't think our members have the idea of gobbling up all the land around but we feel our land base could be somewhat bigger.

I made a comment when I first came to the co-op that I thought there would be three membership changes over the first five years. But there has been no change-over. For 11 guys to be together ten years, you know, it amazes me. So that reflects what type of individuals are here. We are surrounded by a highly individualistic farming society and for co-ops to survive — well, we are definitely a minority.

I think co-ops are a good option, not the only option, but one good option to deal with the lack of people on the farm. This is a prime example of it and I think you have to thank some of the original members of the Matador Co-op Farm for that. They could have received more money for this land when they sold it in 1974 than they did through the Saskatchewan Land Bank. But they were interested in passing it on to their sons and so they did. They took less money to do so. Now 11 members live here plus some of the past members. But, it could have been just one person who owned this land base. So that's a prime example in my mind of how to keep more people in a rural area.

Times vary too. You know, when we first started out, as I look back, likely one of the best things is that we had a few hardships. We got froze out three of the first four years. We had a couple of fairly serious fires. We had a bit of a catastrophe when our shop blew down in a windstorm while we were building it. Those things can either make or break any individuals that are living or working together. And what it seemed to do here, is it seemed to tie the group together. It really carried on from there. Maybe those are some of the reasons this group has been tied so closely together. The co-op has come through some hard times — although my grandfather wouldn't call what we've had hard times.

Now, we'll also go through other periods. As people get more money they become more individualistic in mind. Co-ops are more common in tough times than in good times. As we go through some of those better periods maybe the co-op will suffer from that, I don't know. But, up until now, there hasn't been lots of money that might make you split up for those reasons.

Being too successful could actually be a hindrance to a co-op. I very much think so. You tend to forget some of the advantages of being co-operative. Sometimes you tend to think that the grass is greener on the other side and maybe want to try doing something else.

Gordie Dawe and Dale Stewart, Matador Farm Pool meeting,
Kyle, Saskatchewan

WALTER AND ROBERT NISBET stand in the dairy barn on a frosty fall morning trying to define the ins and outs of agriculture and, in particular, dairy farming. Robert explains it: "It's like running hurdles when someone keeps moving them around on you."

The Ardoch Co-op Farm was formed in 1965 by the Nisbet family. Together, three families farm 2,700 acres and keep 100 head of beef and dairy cattle. Not only do the members — which in this Co-op includes the women — share the work but they also share a large house. Constructing one large building and partitioning it into apartments lowered the expense of materials, heating, and plumbing.

Walter explains that, unlike many co-ops, the continuation of Ardoch is not a problem since the children of Ardoch are gifted shares in the organization when they become 18.

WALTER: With a co-operative, as times change the situation changes and you have to be flexible. I've noticed that with our family, if you can start talking about something early enough so that you can develop your opinions together it is a whole lot better for the harmony of the group than if you develop an opinion and say: "I've already thought this through and this is the way we are going to do it." There's no room for give and take unless you have the discussions early on.

It's said quite a lot that if times are tough then you co-operate and if times are buoyant then you go your own way. I'm inclined not to believe that. My theory is that the co-op situation is out there. People are co-operating together, they just haven't formalized their agreements. With the high cost of machinery more pronounced now than it has ever been, it is certainly more financially beneficial to use machinery co-operatively. Your cost per hour is much lower if you spread it over more hours.

I'm quite biased as farm co-operatives go. As far as I'm concerned a person is crazy not to do it that way. I think it's a better way to go. You have more people on the land and you've got, I think, a better kind of production. If you're farming umpteen quarters of land, I'll venture to say your yield per acre is not as good as a farm where each field is a major share of the farm operation.

Traditionally farmers have been interpreted as being strong individualists. They want to do their own thing when they want to do it. It is certainly a strong feeling among farmers that they would like to own their own line of equipment so that it is there in the yard and they can use it when they want. They don't want to be dependent on somebody else. So, if you can farm that way, that is likely the first choice.

But, if you start paying 130,000 dollars for a combine, as you do now, where are you going to collect enough capital to start in the farming business without going in on a joint venture with somebody? You have to have financial backing beyond what is usually available to the individual. Then, of course, you also have to collect the land base. We bought a section in 1954 for 15,000 dollars. The value is now somewhere around 150,000 dollars per quarter. That's 40 times higher.

So, certainly a co-operative is one of the alternatives that provides for quite a bit of freedom. I think you likely have more freedom in a co-operative than when you are working on your own. You have joint decision-making, which is a valuable tool. You can weigh the situation among yourselves and stand a better chance of coming up with the best conclusion. Whereas, if you rely on your own judgement you may miss a few crucial factors and that might be fatal.

Robert and Walter Nisbet, Ardoch Co-op Farm,
Success, Saskatchewan

DENNIS LAXDAL   Every other week the seven members of the Lakeside Machinery Co-op gather in the office built into the second floor of their quonset near Dafoe, Sask. Dennis Laxdal tells me that numerous similar meetings led to the formation of the Co-op in 1971.

While the membership has changed over the years, the majority are still original members or their sons. All of the members own their own land, but they pool machinery, labour, and grain sales. While an average individual farmer will spend about $200,000 on equipment, the seven members of Lakeside estimate that their total investment in equipment and buildings comes to no more than $500,000.

DENNIS: We got started with seven older farmers who decided that the way things were going it would be quite a bit cheaper to share machinery and labour costs. We discussed it for a year before we organized. We were all getting older and some of us had young sons who were interested in farming. We thought that this was one way of getting the younger fellas started. We started with eight young farmers and six of them are still with us. Now we are almost completely into the second generation.

Right now we farm 35.5 quarters — not much more than what we started with in 1971. The only problem we are having is cash flow...the same as everybody else. Controlling expenses seems to be a bit harder to do than it would be as individuals. Each member is in a bit of a different financial situation. Some are paying for land, others are renting land, others are renting Land Bank land and don't have the same expenses. The cash-flow varies with each member. Still, I think the members of the group are better off, particularly the younger fellas because they wouldn't be farming otherwise. This spring we discussed whether we should buy land as a group. That created quite a bit of discussion because those who are already making high land payments aren't interested in getting into any further debt.

Interest rates are still too high. And although the Saskatchewan government is subsidizing young farmers with 8 per cent loans, I don't feel they're going to be able to start

out without more assistance from somewhere.

If some of these problems were solved, farming would have a bright future. Take transportation: I know it's a problem but I don't know how they can expect farmers to pay the freight rates. We wanted to keep the Crow. We need guarantees, but guarantees don't mean much when it comes to government because governments change. The boys in the co-op that have Land Bank land are having problems now because the provincial government changed and this government doesn't like the Land Bank concept.

Co-ops have lots of advantages as far as the decision-making is concerned. It happens quite frequently that someone has a strong opinion that not everyone agrees with. Then that member has to accept the fact that the majority rules. Some of the ones who quit the co-op, I guess, that's what bothered them. When a member quits we either give him some equipment or pay him out in equity. That can affect our operations quite a bit — the same when a member retires. It's a continuing thing. You have to balance off the new members coming and those leaving. Right now we are in a position of having more machinery than we should because people come and go.

I'm surprised that there are not more co-ops. I'm surprised that more of them didn't start up when we did and that there have not been more since. I suppose it might be because farmers are queer individuals. They are pretty independent. Times seem to have changed as well. People's thinking seems to have changed. They are more individualistic. There's been a big change in government in this province. That's a change in thinking from left of centre to a freewheeling right-wing government. That bothers me more than the economy.

I really don't know what is going to have to happen before things get changed around. I think this co-op could last the lifetime of these young members unless something drastic happens. It's a better way to go.

Dennis Laxdal and Lakeside Machinery Co-op,
Dafoe, Saskatchewan

CHRIS MEWHORT reminisces about the origins of the name, "The Self-Reliance and Hard Struggle Co-op." Originally, in the early 1970s, Halina Zaleska, Richard Mewhort and Chris had wanted to name the farm after Louise Lucas, "one of the grand old ladies of the CCF." But for months the Department of Co-operatives turned down the application. Eventually, it was discovered that someone didn't think the name appropriate. The trio tried again, this time testing the mettle of the officials with a quote from Mao Tse-tung.

As it turns out, The Self-Reliance and Hard Struggle Co-op couldn't be a better fit. The Co-op, near Sonningdale, Sask., has seen members come and go and has struggled to keep its one and a half-section mixed farm afloat. While initially it included people from outside and with various backgrounds, today it is a family co-op.

CHRIS: During the last war, when a fighter pilot went down or was killed they used the phrase "he bought the farm" to describe what happened to him. I always wondered why they used that expression until we purchased this operation. Now I know why "buying the farm" is a synonym for complete and total disaster.

We chose this name because that's the way it is. You have to rely on yourself because you can't afford to pay anyone else to do your work and the hard struggle comes in because there is nothing that comes easy on the farm anymore. You have to fight all the time just to stay in one place.

Our father had been in one of the first co-operatives after the war. But as that co-op made money it continued to shrink. Eventually the very thing that had made them so successful — the co-op — was dropped because some members wanted to farm individually.

We always grew up with the idea that it was better to farm with other people than by yourself. Co-op was a good word in our house. We were penniless and broke, so we thought the thing to do was to farm together. I was raising pigs and going to school. We thought we'd start with pigs and, when they made a lot of money, we'd branch into other things. We'd get bigger and bigger and have more people. That's what we

fully expected to happen because we'd seen it happen before.

But the economics of farming in Saskatchewan changed. Input costs just rose at a much faster rate than gross income did. The result is that it has been impossible to make any money at all. Anyone that purchased or rented a farm in the last ten years has found it impossible to make any headway at all.

We purchased our assets for about 10 per cent of what it would cost us now. That gave us a good break. When we purchased our grain farm we became tenants of the government through the Land Bank. That was another good break. We have managed to make some good breeding-stock sales, which have added to our net income. We haven't had a major disaster . . . the barns haven't burned down. Huge things, expensive things, have not happened to us so we've managed to get along.

The other thing is that we take a very, very, low standard of living. We've lived for ten years with enough to eat, a reasonable amount of clothes, both new and second-hand, and what you would term as "mad" spending money, maybe 50 dollars a year above that.

A lot of people would not be at all satisfied with that low level. They would say that the farm, one way or another, has got to give them another 10,000 dollars a year. Of course, if those people had been farming across the road from us, they'd be gone. That's the advantage we have. We retract our standard of living till it's far under what other people will accept. It puts our costs of production lower and lower and we can continue to stay on here. It's surprising what you can do without when you decide to stay on here. I suspect a great deal of people would have flung up their hands and liquidated their farm by now.

We started with four people. Then a month later two more people joined. Three left within the first few years. They got back what they put in, which in one case was fairly substantial and in the other case was minimal. Our bylaws say people have to be paid out over a ten-year period so that the farm is not jeopardized. One member, not wanting to cause us any financial problems, said he would take half of

The Self-Reliance and Hard Struggle Co-op,
Sonningdale, Saskatchewan

the lump sum, which really helped.

This farm was essentially launched on 2,000 dollars. If you'd gathered all the original members and shook out their pockets, that's what you would have come up with. Now it's worth around 400,000 dollars. Ten years ago, when people said you needed 100,000 dollars, we did it with 2,000 dollars. We were exceptionally lucky. Being in financial difficulty has nothing to do with efficiency. In almost all cases farmers having financial difficulty in Saskatchewan are having it because they are trying to buy their farms.

How long we are able to farm is solely up to the banker. If the bank chooses not to extend us any more credit when we're losing money, or demands payment even when prices are very very low, then we probably couldn't survive another year or so with prices under the costs of production. In which case our farm would become vacant because there is no market for sale right now. And we believe that the bank understands this really well and will continue to have us here with the appearance of being semi-prosperous and giving them perhaps 80 or 90 per cent of what they want in the hopes that good times will return and we can pay everything off. This place has technically been for sale for the last four years and we have had no serious offers.

Only the quick and the nimble are going to survive over time. I guess it's the same with any other small business and I find it a challenge to try to be quick and nimble. If you take the pessimistic view, everyone is going to be bankrupt sooner or later and it's a question of how late you're going to be. It would be really nice to be the last one to go.

If you take the optimistic view, next year will be better and there will be plenty of rain and the price of grain will go to astronomical heights and everything will be rosy. I suppose I fall somewhere in between those two views.

HALINA ZALESKA is a member of the Self-Reliance and Hard Struggle Co-op near Sonningdale, Sask., where she is a specialist in the handling of pigs. Equipped with special overalls and boots for the confinement barn, I watched her in action and marvelled at how this small, fast-paced, 33-year-old gave no-nonsense direction to 600-pound boars.

Halina is proud of saying that the co-op has the largest registered Lacombe herd in the world — a total of 174 sows. Although she grew up in the city, her vocabulary now consists of phrases like "pre-weaning mortality" and "reproductive performance."

HALINA: When I was in university I met Chris and he had this wild scheme about setting up a co-operative farm. I had 2,000 dollars to invest. I made the mistake of investing it. Initially I was going to work in the city and just come out on weekends. I was working on a degree in chemistry. Now you'd never catch me going back to the city. In the city, especially in something like chemistry, you spend too much time doing mental work and never give your muscles a stretch. Other than that, the smell of the city is something that I can't get used to...the exhaust fumes. That may sound funny coming from a pig farmer.

But I like pigs. Pigs are smarter than some people I know, especially politicians. I like the challenge of handling them. If you're good you can always be better. If you can wean 15 piglets per sow, you can work for 18. Pigs are management intensive. And because you work with them they become tame — tamer than some of the cats and dogs I've met. Sometimes you have physical problems, but mostly you do things differently. You do it your own way.

The thing that affects me the most as a woman...one of the things...is that attitudes haven't changed. I'm not eligible for a Farmstart loan. I was at first, but once they found out that I was actually living with Chris — it took them two kids to figure that one out — then I was considered to be a married woman and I ceased to exist for Farmstart's purposes. The Saskatchewan Hog Assurance Program works the same way. You're covered for so many pigs per farmer and,

when you count farmers, wives don't count no matter how many hours they spend in the barn. That stuff just doesn't make sense because the eligibility requirements are that you spend the major portion of your time working in the barn. So that cuts out housewives in the first place. And it's no harder to check whether a wife works in the barn than it is to check whether a sister or daughter does. They're covered, but wives aren't.

There are other small problems too. For instance, it takes a while for the average salesman who wants to sell hog or farm equipment to realize that he doesn't have to ask for my husband. There was one particularly obnoxious one who definitely wanted to talk to my husband. So when Chris came out, the salesman said he was selling hog equipment. Chris simply said: "Oh, you'll have to talk to my wife," and walked off. It helps to have a supportive husband. If I get phone calls and someone asks for the boss, I put on the kids.

I have full days, that's for sure. From six to eight in the morning I feed the pigs. Then I come into the house and get the kids ready to go to the sitters and to school. Then about nine-thirty I get out and do the breeding. It's all hand-mated so you have to chase a boar into the pen with a group of sows and check for heat and then breed the one in heat to exactly the right boar. We have carefully worked out the breeding program. Then after that I work with the pigs in the farrowing crates. Any new litters have to have iron shots and teeth clipped, that kind of thing. They need to be castrated and tattooed. I treat for scours and take temperatures and check for mastitis.

Then after lunch, I do the same thing in the nursery barn with the weaned pigs. I also treat any sows that need to be treated. After that there is a special project for each day of the week. One day the sows have to go into the farrowing crates. The next day might be to get a weanling room ready...another might be to do pregnancy tests and vaccinations...another might be to wean. Then Friday you get the farrowing room washed and Saturday and Sunday afternoon you spend with the kids. Time after supper belongs to the kids too...and to the dishes.

Halina Zaleska,
Sonningdale, Saskatchewan

JIM MUMM   The members of Hazelridge Co-op have recently built new log homes on their quarter near Shellbrook, Sask. While the houses are several city lots away from each other, they are part of the same yard. When the Co-op was started in 1976 its members camped out in tents the first year while trying to get the farm operation off the ground on an investment of little more than a few thousand dollars.

During the last few years the Co-op, which is also an organic farm, has grown alfalfa and raised leafcutter bees. It now rents an additional quarter of land besides the quarter it owns. Jim Mumm, an original member, says the Co-op believes in intensive and diversified farming.

JIM: Six of us got the idea and formed the co-op through the Department of Co-operatives in 1976. Four of these members have now left and two more have joined. We formed it partly so we could start farming because none of us had much money. There was also the feeling that a co-op would be a better lifestyle than individual farms. Both of those still apply. If we farmed individually, each one of us would need just about the same equipment that we have now as a group, which would double our costs. We can also specialize labour and do more things with a co-op.

There were some personality clashes and some of the former members weren't from farm backgrounds and found that farming wasn't what they expected. They had an idealized vision of going back to the land. Some people had trouble with the lack of privacy as well.

If we'd started an operation individually we'd still be very badly in debt. As it is, we haven't been in debt until this year and now we have a small debt for a new tractor. We try not to borrow any money if we can help it. We started out small and only increased as we had money to do so. Leafcutter bees have been profitable in the last five years so that helped a lot to keep us going.

We have poor sandy soil and raising alfalfa seed on this soil has really improved it. We've seen tremendous change in the structure of the soil. It doesn't blow anymore. Wind erosion is very bad in this area, but we've pretty well stopped that on our land. As far as we are concerned, if you have to destroy the land to farm you may as well quit. We found a way to make a living without damaging our land. But we know a lot of people have to keep producing because of their debt load. A lot of the old ways of farming are being lost because people are so dependent on chemicals. People are no longer being taught how to farm and they are being led to believe that they are not hurting themselves on their land. We've talked to a lot of the old fellows to get some ideas. We are always fighting weeds and constantly learning.

I suspect that when people realize they have problems, like loss of organic matter, we'll see partial solutions like chemical summerfallow rather than mechanical summerfallow. But I don't think that we are going to see any big change to organic farming on the prairies. I think the best we can hope for is a little bit of common sense, like integrated pest management that cuts chemical use and gives the same or better results than the old "dump the chemical on" school of farming. Organic farms are more work, more thinking. The farms now are mostly too large and it sure is easy just to go to the Ag Rep and ask what to spray. It's very simple.

I've never said that we'd never use chemicals. But my philosophy is, when in doubt don't spray. Most farmers and government publications lean towards "when in doubt spray." I guess that's the difference between us and them.

Hazelridge Co-op Farm: Maggie and Jim Mumm, David Palm,
Shellbrook, Saskatchewan

LARRY FREY   The co-operation between the seven members of Agri-Pool goes back past the day the organization was formed in 1971. Some of the farmers had worked together on an ad hoc basis for years and had shared equipment and hands during seeding and harvest. All the members of Agri-Pool live within a few miles of each other, south of Lestock, Sask. When financial problems began to weigh heavily on some of them, co-operative farming was the natural outgrowth.

Together the members farm ten sections, the same amount they originally pooled. Much of the land is owned by the individuals, although Agri-Pool owns a small parcel. Member Larry Frey says these days the co-op is successful. The main concern, typically enough, is how to roll over the land and the organization to the second generation.

LARRY: We got the name Agri-Pool from agriculture and working together. It was a shortened version of everything we were doing and it was supposed to catch the ear. Agri-Pool got started for different reasons for different people. In my case I wanted a change of lifestyle. I didn't want to work all the time. I wanted to do a bit of travelling. I wanted to enjoy my family some. I wanted to get into farming in a bigger way because I like farm management. Perhaps a sense of security was part of it as well.

The farm is labour efficient and very equipment efficient. The average investment of equipment to land in Saskatchewan is one dollar to four dollars. If you own four dollars' worth of land, you have to have one dollars' worth of equipment — this is what farmers are doing. But our co-op is operating at a ratio of one dollar of equipment to nine dollars of land.

We own our own land and our co-op owns land. We work on a cash return per cultivated acre that we have in the co-op plus an hourly rate. I suppose each family earns about 20,000 dollars or more in net income. It's not that we are making any great amount of money but the fact that we are keeping a fair percentage of the money we handle. It's mainly our efficiency in equipment. We only have

two trucks, two combines, two swathers, one drill and one repair shop. We were looking for an easier way out or a cheaper way out, I guess. The cost of machinery per farm unit was far less in a co-op. Individually we would need seven of each machine.

Efficiency means two things to me. It means that we are using our finances well, which means that for every dollar we are taking in we are keeping a fair piece of that dollar for ourselves. It means that in terms of labour we can accomplish a lot. It means if we need a whole family out there to chase cows we have them. When you are efficient you have quality of life — you have some dollars and some time.

I've done more for my education since I've had Agri-Pool working for me than I ever did during those eight years that I went to school. Time means something to me. I'd never seen the ocean until I was a member of Agri-Pool. I didn't want to go and see it when it was freezing. I think the family farm is efficient. But we in the co-op have become more efficient without squeezing other farmers out.

We could live in one big yard and a little community and it would be even more efficient. But I think that's pushing the law of averages just a little too far. That might cause some friction. We've had our problems, but we've never come to blows. We don't swear that much at each other. There have been some silences perhaps, and hasty words, but I think looking back, I doubt if we've spent two per cent of our time squabbling. We sure as hell disagreed alright, but it has been a pretty good disagreement. A few bottles of rum have changed hands on bets.

Agri-Pool is successful. It is doing what we wanted it to. At one time the whole co-op philosophy was really important and it still is but I suspect that it is not as important anymore. It seems to be a fact of life that when you become financially stable or secure in your life then you start to look at yourself like an independent human being. If we have a problem it is that we have become too successful.

Some people or institutions like Revenue Canada refuse to differentiate between a co-op farm and a corporate farm. But there is a difference. In a co-op each person has as much right or authority as any other person. In a corporate farm the golden rule applies: "He who has the money talks."

Revenue Canada recognizes us as a co-op farm alright but they tax us as if we were a corporate farm. Yet the Wheat Board has recognized us. All of our names are in one permit book. If there are any payments made it is on the basis of seven farmers through one book. When it comes to provincial grants or space in a community pasture, although we are recognized as a co-op, they treat us as if we were only three. So, if each individual is allowed 50 cows in the community pasture we are only allowed 150. They consider us to be no more than three. The same occurs with corporate farms. I suspect that the lawmakers are still governed by family farms and family farms are nervous about co-op farms, Hutterite farms, and corporate farms. I think that's the basic reason.

The other problem we have is with the continuation of Agri-Pool. It cost us 15 dollars to buy into it plus the equipment and cattle that we had at the time. Now we've managed so well that each one of our shares is worth about 140 dollars. That's our equity. There was no market value on day one. It has increased through inflation and it is pretty well debt free. Being treated as a corporation becomes a substantial disadvantage because we lose our right to roll over our land to our sons and daughters without paying capital gains. Still, it's cheaper to do it this way than to go farming on your own. I haven't a clue as to what will happen to Agri-Pool. In the beginning I never dreamt it was going to be near as successful as it is.

Looking at the situation now I don't think there are ever going to be that many co-ops in Saskatchewan. The efficiencies of a co-op are obvious, but it doesn't seem that the idea is catching hold. People are interested, but for some reason it's difficult for a farmer to decide to work with someone else. I think that people who farm are trying to get away from it all. They don't want to work with their neighbour because they know they are going to have to sort out hassles.

The direction of agriculture as I see it is that the well-established families will pass down their farm from genera-

George Frey, Agri-Pool,
Lestock, Saskatchewan

tion to generation. Those that are not well-established will have to leave the farm and the farms will continue to get bigger. To what size I have no idea. There is no limit to horsepower. A 100-foot cultivator is no big deal anymore. Maybe the result will be agribusiness or some sort of feudal system. There'll be a loss. Society will be urban-business and labour oriented.

Man is a product of evolution and all this has been based on some form of agriculture whether it has been root-pickers or meat-eaters. Our basics are in agriculture. Human beings seem to have the characteristics that they want a piece of land...like animals they like to stake out a piece of ground. If our society is raised in an apartment there are going to be some unsatisfied yearnings going on.

Farmers are pretty stable. Generally speaking they are the last ones to take up arms. They're pretty easy to handle. They are so busy out there looking at the sun and the sky and ground and worrying about the furrow that they're turning over, that they don't pay much attention to what is happening to them.

Bigger and Better?

The prairie countryside is strewn with stories about "big farmers." If nothing else these coloured commentaries are an indication of the tension that exists between the large farmer and the small.

People talk, for instance, about the large farmer who had so much land and equipment that when his hired hand decided to quit, and abandoned the four-wheel-drive tractor in the farthest field he could find, the farmer didn't even notice it was missing until he stumbled on it the next spring. Then there was the large farmer who had so much land that in his rush to get his crop in he forgot to seed a recently acquired quarter. Yet another story goes around about a large farmer who had such volumes of crop that he could afford *not* to close the doors on the storage bins: it didn't seem to matter if the snow and rain dampened his grain.

There's no doubt that these stories are exaggerated. Still, the large prairie producers were often careful to warn me not to believe any of them. One farm woman who helped her husband cultivate umpteen acres explained: "When people joke and ask us whether we forget to farm pieces of our land, I just tell them that you don't have your children all at once. You have them one at a time and you get to know them individually. It's the same with the land."

The large farmers I chatted with, although somewhat guarded because of community pressure, were all very friendly and willing to tell me their views on agriculture and agribusiness. Initially they seem no different than the average producer. They work hard and harbour hopes of

maintaining their operation and safeguarding a parcel of land for their children. Most of them started out small and through a combination of economic pressure, management decisions, proper timing, and luck have been able to enlarge their operations.

It is difficult to define exactly what makes a farmer large. Land needs vary from region to region. In some southern prairie areas, with prime grain-growing land, anything over four or five sections is relatively large. In other locales a farm over eight sections is large. Capital investment is another barometer, with more than $500,000 in land, equipment, and buildings tipping the scale.

At this point in time large farms are generally family-owned corporations. As yet, few corporations outside of agriculture have invested in primary production. A number of farmers and experts speculate that once the land is concentrated among large family operators outside companies will continue the cycle by amalgamating production even further.

The economics of farming encourage expansion. Larger operations mean more volume to meet production costs, but they also mean higher interest payments, more inputs such as fertilizer and chemicals, and more and larger equipment. That in turn increases the need for more land, renewing the vicious economic circle. It's not that these farmers are able to produce more per acre than the small farmer, but that producing larger volumes enables them better to withstand fluctuations in prices and costs. In addition, they have the security to ensure a lengthy credit line. While there is no doubt that they too are able to overextend through borrowing, the banker stands to lose much more by foreclosing on a large operation in times of depressed land prices. Who is going to buy a 10 or 20-section chunk if the large farmer goes under? Rather than have to divide the land and incur extra expenses, plus perhaps pay for the costs of idle land, the banker prudently waits out the financial rough spot.

Large farmers exude the image of self-made people. They are the epitome of the rugged individualist and talk a lot about ambition and competition. All farmers are consumers, but large farmers are larger consumers. They tend to use more agricultural chemicals and fertilizer per acre. Where small producers spend a yearly average of $496 on chemicals, large farmers spend $3,237. These are only averages, remember, and most large operators I spoke to spend over $10,000 a year on chemicals.

Many large farmers use the extremely volatile anhydrous ammonia, a nitrogen fertilizer proved to destroy micro-organisms in the soil, although the exact extent of damage caused is still a matter of debate. The equipment they use is larger and the weight of it is causing concerns about soil compaction. Corporate farmers are also able to afford the latest advances in technology and at times combine forces with educational and research institutes to experiment on new practices such as zero-till or embryo transplants. These farmers know that their survival depends on volume-selling.

One such entrepreneurial farmer is Don Miller, whose family operates Miller Brothers Running MB Stock Farm Inc., which includes a 300-head herd of Chianina breeding stock and a 500-head feedlot near Saskatoon, Sask. He uses embryo transplants to produce breeding stock, a technique touted as one of the most advanced procedures in the cattle industry. In the age of genetic engineering and factory farms, embryo transplant laboratories inside cattle barns may become much more prevalent.

Don Miller has been involved in the process for the last four years and the Running MB has shipped embryos to various countries abroad. First, Don picks a valuable animal to breed. Then, through hormonal injections the animal is prompted to "superovulate" and produce a multiplied number of eggs. Twelve hours after she comes into heat, the cow is artificially inseminated with the semen of a prize bull, three times over 36 hours. Seven days later Don herds the animal into a squeeze shoot, injects a tranquilizer into the cow's lower spine, covers his arm in a plastic glove, inserts his hand, then a catheter, flushes liquid into the uterus and begins milking or massaging it to remove embryos from the walls.

When the fluid is extracted the embryos flow with it. The collection continues for an hour and may produce 10, 20, 40 or, as on one occasion, as many as 60 embryos. The embryos, once checked under a microscope for fertility, can be either transplanted immediately into a surrogate cow through a ten-minute surgical operation or frozen for future use. The success rate without freezing is 70 per cent and once frozen drops to 50 per cent, according to Don. So far he has frozen embryos for as long as four years, but he speculates that they could be frozen eternally. As for the surrogate cow, he has used the same animal as many as four times. The foot-long surgical incisions attest to the years of service. Don says a superovulating cow, the donor animal, lasts about five or six years and is searched for embryos every two months. After every search the breeder cow is given a drug to induce spontaneous abortion in case all of the embryos have not been collected.

The method speeds the process of procreation and, consequently, the improvement of blood lines. The volume of animals also means more money, more often, for prize breeding stock. In the time that it takes a cow to produce a single offspring naturally, embryo transplants could produce 150 siblings. The price tag of a single embryo is about $2,500 and Don says that a calf produced through transplants must be sold for no less than $3,000 or $4,000.

Wayne Arrison of Bassano, Alta., is another large farmer who is bringing new technology and new practice to bear on his farming tasks. For the last few years Wayne has been continuous-cropping his 14 sections using zero-till, a method that eliminates summerfallow and cultivation. The cost in equipment is heavy but Wayne says it's worth it because he feels that he is preserving the soil. His 625-horsepower RITE tractor weighs 63,000 pounds, is 18 feet wide and a single tire is worth $2,500. The Pioneer drills are 12 feet high, weigh 33,000 pounds each and together cost about $240,000. Still, the farm produces the revenue needed to pay for the million-dollar investment in equipment. In an average year Arrison Farms Ltd. grosses over a

138

Doug Bryan,
Central Butte, Saskatchewan

million dollars in sales and Wayne says his family's net income fluctuates around the $100,000 mark.

Large farmers are defined, however, by more than an interest in new and ambitious practices. There is also a matter of attitude. For instance, the larger the farmer the more the loathing of marketing boards or the concept of orderly marketing. Taking the guesswork out of supply, demand, and price is the last thing corporate farmers want or need. Instead they prefer to wait out low-price periods, knowing that when prices do rise there will be substantial gains through volume-selling. Low prices often create a drop in land prices as well, providing large producers with the perfect opportunity to expand holdings. A number of corporate farmers told me that they have indeed added to their land base during recent years: a time when most small producers were trying to hang on to their shirts.

While there are a number of marketing boards operating in Canada, orderly marketing, which in its purest form is a formula that sets commodity prices according to farmers' costs of production, does not exist. However, marketing boards and commissions that try to regulate price and supply do exist for a few commodities such as poultry and milk. The Canadian Wheat Board helps to assure grain sales and an average annual price. While some producers think the Board should handle all sales, eliminating private traders, corporate farmers balk at the thought. Many point to the completely unregulated and open market in the United States as a panacea. Unfortunately, rural U.S.A. is losing thousands of farmers every month. Remaining operations are large and capital-intensive.

Larger farmers also benefit from a number of advantages that small farmers do not have. For instance, one farmer explained to me as he leaned on one of his semi-trailer trucks that he sometimes hauls grain 180 miles. On occasion he has had number-three-grade grain and has hauled it for hours to sell it to a company elevator where he could get top price for a large volume of a lower grade. The number-three is then disguised and mixed in with a better grade. The resulting mix is of lower quality, but still meets the standard and no one is the wiser.

Across the prairies farm groups are split between members who believe that bigger is better and those who think that the loss of farmers is detrimental to communities and production. The split is noticeable in the prairie Wheat Pools, for instance, which were initially created by farmers to protect themselves from the vagaries of big business and the open market. The Pools actively participated in changes to the Crow's Nest Pass Freight Rates. In the process frustrated small producers were left wondering whose side the "co-opteds" were on. The Pools' advertising campaigns lean heavily on promoting farming as a business, chatting up computer technology and large equipment and ignoring issues such as land size, commodity prices, rural depopulation, and soil conservation. The Pools' ads state that the modern farmer "means business." It's little wonder that the corporate farmers I spoke with had no quarrel with the Pools.

These days the most confident farmers are those with large holdings. While they agree that commodity prices are low, they are not panicking. The assurance of their future is borne out by statistics, which leave no doubt that farms are getting larger.

In 1961 farms with more than two sections of land and the highest capital investment accounted for only 2 per cent of farmers on the prairies. In 1981 that figure had risen to 15 per cent of farmers, and farmers with eight quarters or more cultivated more than 30 per cent of prairie farmland, almost triple the 1961 figure. In Saskatchewan 28 per cent of farmers own more than two sections and farm 57 per cent of the land.

While farm numbers decline, the number of large farms is on the increase. On the prairies, close to 20,000 farmers left the land between 1971 and 1981. But the prairies actually lost more than 27,000 medium-sized producers while gaining almost 5,000 large farmers and more than 2,000 hobby farms under 240 acres.

A similar picture emerges with production levels. In Canada 25 per cent of farmers produce 75 per cent of farm commodities, with the top 1 per cent accounting for 19 per cent. One-half the wheat acreage sales comes from 21,000 farms. Half of the country's pig production comes from 2,800 farms. Half of its potato acreage is on 363 farms and two-thirds of turkey gross sales comes from 157 farms.

The story behind prairie farm incomes is much the same. It's estimated that 37 per cent of farmers earn less than $15,000 a year from all sources, whether on or off-farm. While the average farm income is $13,000 — which is below the poverty level for a farm family of four — 28 per cent of farmers earn less than $12,000. Another 10 per cent fall below $5,000 a year. On the other side of the scale, 13 per cent of farmers earn more than $45,000 a year. The income-spread between the highest and the lowest paid farmers proves that there are economic classes amongst farmers much as there are among urban people. It also shows how much money, and how little, some farmers are willing to make.

The tension between large and small farmers is likely to continue as farm consolidation increases to the year 2000. One small farmer explained his feelings about it as he pointed out how his land was bordered on three sides by a 30-section neighbour. "It's like being watched by a hawk." He knows that given an opportune moment he too may be picked off by the highest bidder.

DOUG BRYAN's 28 sections — about 18,000 acres — are spread between the home base in Central Butte and the edge of the Regina Plains near Moose Jaw, Sask. The Bryan family hands out pens with the slogan "The Most Fertile Farm in the West." Doug and his wife, Marilyn, chuckle with pride about the number of children and grandchildren they have. Together they have created a second corporation, Future Farms Ltd., to act as an agent in transferring the land.

Doug says it is hard to estimate his worth because of factors like speculation and inflation, but he imagines that he operates a $10 million show. One year he recalls that he paid $57,000 in taxes. And he says that during the winter the phone rings off its hook with calls about potential land purchases. Marilyn plays a major role on the farm. She keeps the books and Doug checks with her about "exactly" how much land D. M. Bryan Farms Ltd. owns.

DOUG: I think a farmer should in his own benefit take his own risk. That's why I never put on hail or crop insurance or any kind of insurance. I figure that this gives me a big advantage because I'm not paying out all that money. I have given myself an advantage by taking the risk. Over the years it has given me an enormous advantage. I've been hailed, but I'm still ahead of the game. It's time-consuming just administering hail insurance, so I take all my own risk.

I started farming in 1946 on the old home farm and my mother backed me on a half-section in 1952 and I grew from that. I just kept buying. I own all these 28 sections — me and the bank. I rented land once but that was unfortunate because the guy took it away from me. He said I had too much land and I wasn't farming it right. So I've believed since that owning the land is best. I'm a happy farmer. I think things should take their natural course and if a guy wants to be a large farmer, that's his business. And if a guy wants to be a small farmer that's his business too. You can make a living on quite a small plot, really.

The problem with agriculture is that most people want more than their share. I think everybody should just let things go as they will on the free market. That means a free market between countries, with no tariffs. I believe in free enterprise, unbridled free enterprise, to put the enterprise back into the whole thing. I'm against the Wheat Board, although it's not a big issue. Every practical man knows that the Wheat Board is here to stay. But I don't want to see any other marketing boards. Free enterprise and let things fall where they may and let people hustle — that's what I believe in and I think a lot of people believe that.

The NDP had the Land Bank and now the Conservatives have eight per cent subsidized loans. Well heavens, I think people should be up in arms. Someone has got to pay for that. Listen, these young people who need backing should have backing from their families, not the government. I'm backing my son. Heaven's sake, I'm not a superman. I'm just a little wee gosling, just like everybody else is. How come I can back my son and put my money where my mouth is?

You're talking to me, eh, the so-called big farmer, but there's a lot of farmers who have a modest amount of land who have a lot of organization and have kept it together for their family. They deserve a lot of respect because they have kept it. There's always those taxes to pay and those bills to grind out, and crop failures. A friend of mine was telling me about this man he admired who had managed to farm a half-section. This man was his example of success because he had made ends meet. You can put that amount of land in your hip pocket. I don't think that's a big feat. I mean, how much management does it take to manage a half-section? His whole life accomplishment was keeping this half-section in good shape. It's not aspiring to do much is it?

If farmers are good managers there's no reason why they shouldn't make it. It's a snap, just a snap. They don't have to be that good managers, they just have to work, W-O-R-K, that's all...just a little bit of work. A little bit of hustle and not being scared of a little bit of risk — that's the key. Anybody can do it. I think that if people lose their farms it is because they haven't worked enough. That's it. And they really lose their farms when they sell them too cheap. A lot of people sold their land a few years ago and they thought

*Doug Bryan and farmworker,
Central Butte, Saskatchewan*

the accumulation of Loblaws or Dominion Stores. Some of these guys just keep building and building. Lots of them get burnt. But, when the economy goes up everybody will start speculating again and land is the same damn thing.

This is what made me. They all run to me around here. I would say I'm probably the bottom line of the land prices around here. What Doug Bryan will pay...this is an egotistical statement but...I'm one of the ones who has set the land value. I paid the top price for this stuff because I wanted this land so badly. I don't feel so good about setting the land prices. I didn't intend it to be that way, I just sort of drifted into that situation. But, around Moose Jaw and Central Butte I would say that a lot of guys have used me as leverage. People claim that I made bids I never made to crank up the price for someone else.

They call me "high finance." If you have a large amount of land you can always sell some of it. The credit line is longer. They'll loan you the moon if you have security and an attitude that you'll pay it back come hell or high water.

This goes right back to attitude, you see, attitude is the key. You hold the whole world in your hand with attitude. That's the key to getting money. If you have the attitude that you'll crawl a thousand miles on broken glass to pay your debt, well, hell, I can get all kinds of money just on my attitude. The banker knows that I'll go to my grave paying and that I have the property. Very simple.

I don't think larger farms are necessarily good or bad, I think it's a reality. There are some tigers out there and there's people with heart that the little guys are going to go to, to sell their land. I have never pushed a sale. Usually people come to me. I've never had to bulldoze anybody into selling. You don't have to, people want the money. One wants the money and the other wants the land. But the people who sold did it to themselves. I didn't make it happen. It's the nature of humans. People can't stand prosperity and when they have a good thing they drop it. It's greed.

paying a hundred dollars an acre was a lot. But, they didn't bank on inflation. Now they're sitting in towns.

The reason agriculture is getting into larger hands is because some people have vision. The average farmer — the word average is a connotation of littleness, really — thinks like a relative of mine who once told me that two sections is enough for anybody. Everybody gets in their head that so much is enough and you're supposed to have only so much. But growth is creeping into agriculture like it's creeping into all other spheres of the economy.

There is such a thing as open-ended accumulation. It don't matter what it is — land, urban property, or business,

LAWRENCE ENGEL started farming in 1955 with three quarters of rented land. Today he farms nine sections by continuous-cropping and is a registered seed-grower near Quill Lake, Sask. He is one of the largest farmers in the area, but his holdings are farmed jointly with his son. In his years of farming Lawrence has owned 17 tractors. These days he owns two four-wheel-drive tractors, one which pulled 56 feet of seed-drill the day I arrived on his farm.

Lawrence makes no effort to hide his pet peeves. He doesn't like welfare, unemployment insurance, income tax, or labour unions. "The problem isn't the cost of living today," he says. "It's the cost of living it up."

LAWRENCE: Farming is certainly going to sort out the men from the boys in the next ten years. I don't know exactly what's coming. We can't keep paying 12 per cent or more every year for equipment. We have to get more for our product. It's got to come to an end. Our costs and income are going to have to stabilize — they've got to be relative, or people are just going to go broke.

The big guy is going to have to be pretty sharp in his figures or it's going to catch up with him too. I think it's going to continue to go bigger and bigger. It's efficient if you have the proper help and the proper financial backing to run it properly. I'm probably doing the work of two men. If someone from the city were to come out here they'd probably think I was crazy. We work 12 to 14 hours a day until the ground freezes.

We wouldn't be better off financially with a smaller farm. We have about 800,000 dollars invested in equipment on this farm. And because we are registered seed-growers we have to keep our land real clean. We have to use a lot of chemical, which is one of our big concerns because of the costs. In a continuous-cropping operation chemicals are a must and if we don't use them we have problems. Our fertilizers and chemical bill last year were in the neighborhood of 70,000 dollars. We use anhydrous ammonia and nitrogen phosphorus. I have no way of knowing whether anhydrous is damaging the soil, except by the soil tests done at the lab in Saskatoon. I have to go by what they tell me. I've probably used it for ten years already.

If I'm continuous-cropping I don't change crops too often. I had barley seven years in a row on one field and I've had wheat four or five years in a row on another. I read everything I can find on anhydrous ammonia but so far I've not been able to find anything that proves it's damaging. The results we've had are tremendous and the convenience of handling it is far above anything else. So we plan on staying with it until it's proven that it is something we shouldn't be using. I suppose that's not the right way of doing it. Maybe we should wait until it's proven safe.

One great big problem is income tax. We have to buy our land with tax-paid money... the dollar that's left over after I pay my income tax. It's getting harder and harder to get a tax-paid dollar in your pocket. When you go and buy a quarter of land for 125,000 dollars you can imagine how much income tax you are going to pay until you clear that debt. Being incorporated has been a help. The main advantage is that we are in a 28 per cent tax bracket rather than an increasing scale.

We cut corners wherever we can. We go to the city to do a lot of our shopping. A lot of our clothes and groceries comes from the city. As far as equipment goes, we shop where we can get the best deal and that might be Melfort, Wynyard, Regina, Saskatoon or Humboldt.

Lawrence Engel and son Kevin,
Quill Lake, Saskatchewan

DAN LUTZ walks quickly from point A to B. The 16 sections of land he continuously crops — 10 of which he owns, the rest is "cash-rented" — mean that there is always lots to do. The land stretches over 15 miles and includes seven farmsteads near Yorkton, Sask. During harvest an 18-person work crew is out in the fields.

The Lutz farm includes in that labour force a semi-truck driver whose work is hauling grain to the bins or to the elevator. The combines all have computers and a number of the five-ton trucks include private-channel radios. The vocabulary is peppered with jargon — seed accuracy, take-up monitors, acreage meters, moisture meters, and down-time. It's finely tuned farming. One of Dan's five sons, Harvey, says it's possible to unload a five-ton truck in eight seconds. But Harvey also admits that the amount of farmwork means that he seldom looks forward to weekends.

DAN: We started off by renting 40 acres in 1955. We bought our first land in 1960 and to top it off it was a dry year. We bought a quarter that year. And two or three years later we bought another, and we've been buying ever since. Our farm really grew in the seventies. One time we bought ten quarters in one lump sum. In 1983 we bought five quarters. We'll chance it anyways. We own about 40 quarters and we have about 1.5 million dollars invested in equipment. An operating loan for one year is about 400,000 dollars.

I'd say we reached our goal. The boys own part of the farm now, that was probably one goal. I've always wanted to be a large farmer. I've believed in productivity. First of all my goal was to have 1,000 acres and then when we kept on buying I thought we'd see if we could make it to 10,000 acres, which we did. So that's it. It gives me enough to do now. Not only that, there's a lot of interest to be paid. In a year we'd be paying around 200,000 dollars in interest. Our gross sales are about a million dollars. At one time a million was a big figure, but nowadays a million isn't much. We started out with debt and we sort of got trained into it.

We cash-rent from people who don't want to sell their land. Cash-rent is not too bad — you're pretty well your own boss. You actually buy it for the time that you rent it. Rent is anywhere from 30 dollars to 50 dollars an acre. Our chemical costs are fairly high, about 50,000 or 60,000 dollars. Fertilizer is about an additional 18 dollars an acre and we pick up directly from the plant ourselves.

Farming is a good life, but it's a hard life. You have to like it. There are long hours and there are always odds and ends that have to be done. My job is to manage all the acreage. I check the crops and see what has to be done.

We don't consider ourselves any different than the small farmers. The only difference is that we have bigger headaches and bigger risks. We do it because we like it. That was my ambition. We have five boys and we always thought if two of them want to farm we'd have some land for them. Maybe the only difference between me and the guy who never got so big is that the smaller guy has more time with his family.

There's a stigma to farming lots of land. They have their ideas and we have ours. Some people aren't quite willing to take the gamble or stick their necks out the way we do. Then some people are always complaining, no matter what. You can't let it bother you. We've had a certain amount of luck. But the big thing is that you always have to go your own way because there's always a lot of criticism. If we could make it, anybody could make it. We started with nothing. We had no favours going our way except hard work and ambition.

When we were going ahead with farming a lot of people just felt that land was too much money. We never took that attitude. We always figured whatever the price, land was never too much. The last bunch of land, we paid 350,000 dollars for three quarters. Prior to that we'd only paid as much as 49,000 dollars a quarter. The first quarter we ever bought was 10,000 dollars.

In some cases now land is so high, though, that you can't meet the payments based on the production. Your other land, land that's paid or was bought for less, helps you to pay for that land.

We don't think we have more than our share. We've never approached a farmer to buy. Nine times out of ten they will

Dan Lutz and harvest crew,
Yorkton, Saskatchewan

come to us and say they want to sell the farm.

One thing is, if you only farm a section and you get behind, you have to sell some land. Well, you're pretty well beat then. In our case, with the volume we have we could sell quite a bit of land and still be okay. The price for grain may be lower, but we are better off because we are dealing in volume. That's what it amounts to. When we buy chemicals and fertilizer there's a big difference in price per gallon when you buy 300 or just 10.

The future is not going to be easy. Just because you're big doesn't mean you have it made. You still have to keep the ship afloat. I think we'll have bigger farms as well as smaller farms because there is a place for everybody.

Right now it is not good because we don't get enough for our product. Maybe we could go broke like some of the others. We might have to sell some of our land or some of our equipment. It could happen to us too. We might have to get smaller instead to keep up with the bills.

WAYNE ARRISON admits that he gets along better with a machine than with a cow. He began farming in 1968 near Bassano, Alta., and likes the challenge of administrating the farm. When the head-work and the books begin to weigh on him, he hops on his huge, custom-built, RITE tractor worth $300,000 U.S. and clears his mind while going around the fields. The tractor, one of a handful on the continent, pulls two 20-foot Pioneer zero or no-till seed-drills plus four tanks of anhydrous ammonia.

Wayne estimates that he spends no more than 100 hours a year on field-work. His three full-time and six part-time hired hands work the fields. Wayne pulls out a map of the farm, pointing to the uniqueness of the layout. The 8,800 acres form an L-shaped chunk broken only by a single municipal road and the occasional powerline.

WAYNE: I think specialization is the trend, but I am absolutely opposed to any marketing boards of any kind. I believe in the open market. That goes for the Canadian Wheat Board as well. Some of its work is beneficial, but I don't think it has been doing as good a job of selling as it should be. It's pretty hard to circumvent the Wheat Board when it comes to wheat. You're pretty well stuck with them. I don't sell any barley to the Board. I sell it all to the local feed market. Rapeseed I sell mostly to the crushers. The same with flax. We keep a fairly high percentage of our grain non-Board so that we have some flexibility.

One of the aspects that has allowed no-till farming to become successful is that the chemicals are more specific than ever before. I use double the amount of chemicals with no-till than I would if I was farming traditionally, but I think the practice of fallowing is far more destructive on the soil than chemicals. Chemical usage is definitely a bigger part of no-till and I don't think the method would succeed without chemicals.

It has certainly been proven that as soon as anhydrous ammonia hits the soil it destroys a certain amount of the soil micro-organisms in a fairly narrow band where it is injected. But there is land that has been anhydrosed for 20 or 30 years now and it is still producing fairly well, so I don't think that it is fair to say that anhydrous ammonia is going to destroy the activity in the soil.

Chemicals are certainly a big concern and farmers should be more concerned than anybody — although they generally aren't. I don't like using as much as I do. Because we are cropping every year you might think that we should be satisfied with half the yield, but that's not sufficient because our fertilizer and chemical costs are high. Seventy-five per cent of the summerfallow crop is probably the break-even point for us and it seems that we'll have no problems achieving that.

We'll certainly have to work out our rotations, but we haven't enough experience with no-till to find out which ones are going to work best. It is not as easy to switch from wheat to barley or vice versa because there is a certain amount of volunteer grain in a no-till operation and it doesn't take much volunteer grain in a sample to drop a grade.

At one time my objective was to be the largest farmer in Alberta. I don't put that very high on my priorities any longer because I found it too stressful on the family to get too big and too involved. But I might buy more land if I thought the economics were advantageous.

It's getting difficult to say a farm our size is still a family farm because of the size and the number of people we employ. But we still consider it a family farm. Larger and larger farms are a positive thing in the sense that if a country wants a cheap food policy, and every government wants one for their nation, then the farms have to become more efficient and they have to become larger. If a government wants a cheap food policy for their nation, they need to affect the lending agencies in such a manner that the farms can expand and get fewer people and more efficient ones on the farm.

I think that larger farms are a positive thing for the farmers too. But if they try to squeeze the efficiency to the point that farmers are going bankrupt at an abnormal rate — and I don't know what that rate is — the land either gets bought up by huge corporations or oil companies or people not actually interested in the production of food. Then I think it will become detrimental. If large farms are efficient, I think that's fine. That's my personal philosophy.

This farm is the result of three generations of efficient and good management. Most of the people that complain about other people's success spent too much time in the bar when they should have been working. They spend their time in idleness. I suppose some of them may have had some bad luck, too.

I don't feel guilty about the amount of land I farm. In this country, where there is so much freedom of choice, I don't feel guilty. I'd feel guilty in a Third World country where they don't have the opportunity.

Wayne Arrison and hired hands Ove Peterson and Kibby Annets, Bassano, Alberta

148

DON MILLER balances a coffee cup on the nearby post and continues with the job at hand. He says that at times he eats lunch without leaving his work. During the next three hours he explains the procedure involved in embryo searches and transplants in cattle, only removing his arm from a cow's rectum long enough to change donors.

Don has a PhD in Veterinary Medicine and calls himself a farmer-rancher. He changes from his beak-brimmed cap to a cowboy hat to portray the dual roles. Along with other members of his family, Don operates Miller Brothers Running MB Stock Farm Inc., which produces breeding stock using the latest technology — embryo transplants — to spur reproduction and consequently the return on investment.

Embryo transplanting is complicated. It includes hormonal injections, laboratory work, surgical procedures, and surrogate cows. Don has received a few kicks while foraging through cows and admits that, at 30, his knees are in bad shape. "I've got disability insurance that would scare you," he chuckles. The pain must be worth the price tag attached to the dramatic increase in volume.

DON: There are a lot of people who are looking into this transplanting procedure. Some of them are beginning to try it, but you have to know what you're doing. I know a guy who didn't have a pregnancy for two years. He couldn't tell the difference between fertilized and unfertilized eggs. Of course, that's a crucial difference.

Things are moving rapidly in this industry. Within ten years, I think, instead of having artificial insemination schools we'll have embryo transfer schools. You know, in the tank in the next room I'm storing 150 calves.

I don't want to make it sound like it will all be scientific. There will still be people who will use just bulls. But it's true that they won't have much of a chance because embryo transplants will provide for a mass market. Right now, this procedure is making some producers very successful. The market is wide open. There are no controls on the production of embryo transplants.

Sure, this procedure has its ups and downs, but I think if we persevere we'll be rewarded. Of course any slump in the livestock market will affect all producers and maybe slow up this method as well. But during a slump in the cattle market the operators that lose out aren't as keen and concise as they should be. The people that are left are the best managers. It's a tough culling system, but it works.

Just as farmers have gotten larger, cattle operators will have to go the same way. You can make more money on volume. There will be more mechanization. We operate this place with very few people and I'm sure that's the way things will be channelled in the future.

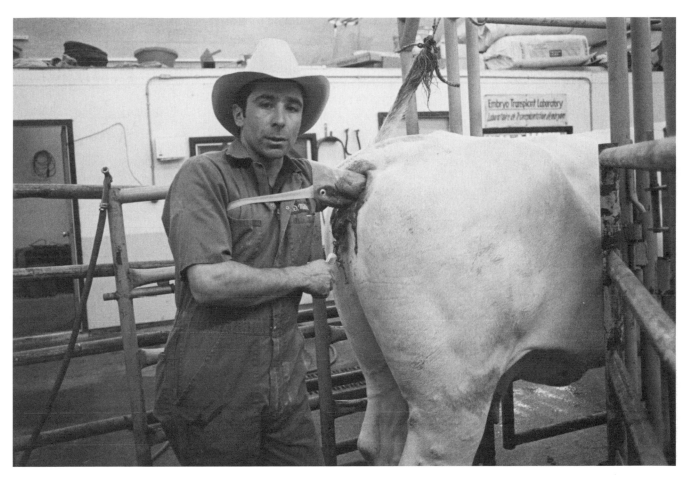

Don Miller,
Saskatoon, Saskatchewan

JOHN KING and his two brothers are third-generation farmers. Their farm of six sections is equipped to handle 5,000 head of custom-fed cattle. The feedlot operation includes a confinement barn where cattle are kept during the last three months of their growth period. While enclosed, each animal gains two to three pounds a day. When full, the barn allows 18 square feet of space for each animal — just enough to sleep, eat, and get fat.

The uniqueness of King & Sons Ranches Ltd., however, is not the confinement barn but rather the feed used. While the company's press release calls the feed "processed bovin wastes," in layperson's language it's called recycled manure. It's one of the few such operations in North America. In fact, what occurs on the King ranch is that the 10,000 pounds of manure that 1,000 confined cattle pass in a day is reused, sufficiently disguised so that the cattle don't recognize it.

The farm hires about 18 people, including an animal technician who administers growth-promoting stimulants and treats disease. King & Sons Ranches Ltd., near High River, Alta., is akin to a "factory" farm.

JOHN: We view ourselves as a company. It's actually a family-owned corporation. If we hadn't formed the company we would have had to pay quite a bit of money out in succession duties when my brother and I took over the land. We formed it in 1965.

Then, being that you are a Limited company you can go direct to dealers for equipment or repairs. If I just phoned up they wouldn't come and work on that semi in my yard. But, being as we are a company they come to us. We don't have to take it in for repairs. You can go directly to the dealer and get dealer prices instead of retail prices. Parts and different stuff, we get a lot cheaper than if we were just individuals going to buy it.

When we built our confinement barn six years ago we looked into the recycling of manure. We built a scraper system to get it out and the manure is coming out every day and we are recycling it and using it as cattle feed. Whenever the manure comes out of the barn the liquid and the solids are together. We separate the two and use the liquid for fertilizer on the land. Then, with the solid, we put it in Harvestores.

We feel that we are getting more benefit from it by using it as feed because actually, when you look at it, on a nutritive point of view everything in it can be used again as feed. The first time around the cattle haven't taken very much out of it. Cattle are poor converters of feed. They take the most amount of feed for every pound of beef. Chickens are one to one, hogs are three pounds of feed to one pound of pork and cattle are seven to one. So a lot of this feed goes through them and you don't get any second shot at it.

The feed going into our barn over there has 13 per cent protein and about 75 per cent total digestible nutrients. Whenever we take the water from the manure and save the solid it comes back at about that: we end up with a product that is 10 per cent protein and 59 per cent total digestive nutrients. So you can take this product and put hay or straw — we use straw — and you have a ration that you can feed straight to cows. We use 10 per cent of the manure rations mixed with other feed. If you go to more than that then you get some reduction in feed consumption.

To consume the amount of ration we make from the manure we need about 1,100 head in the confinement barn. You need a whole bunch of cows to take the quantity. I can put 1,000 cattle in the confinement barn and in the wintertime I can crowd it up and go to 1,100 which would put them down to about 16 square feet. Because they are in close quarters, to avoid disease you make sure they get all of their shots when they come in so that you get them started on feed right. These are preventative shots. We implant for growth. We use one called Ralgro: it's a growth promoter and it works differently than Synovex, which is a regular hormone which makes them eat more and make better use of the feed they do eat. We also use an antibiotic like Tetracycline in the feed for the first 21 days. Then we use mass medication if there is a problem — to treat disease.

I think this type of operation — the recycling of manure — is going to catch on. We'll see more and more work being done by one person — larger farms and fewer people working on them. I still think that you'll have the family farm, but I think that they will be larger family farms. More like this one. You'll see the amalgamation of farmers. I think the larger farms are more productive. Usually the people that are bigger, the bigger operator, tend to do things better as a rule. He has the machinery to do it. People that only farm a half-section or a section don't have the cash return to be able to afford the proper equipment.

Barry and John King,
High River, Alberta

BERT WILDFONG sits behind his office desk in the quonset on his farm near Craik, Sask., pausing sometimes in conversation to swat flies. Bert is a promoter of "laissez-faire" agriculture and a founding member of Palliser Wheat Growers, a group formed in 1970 to fight for the abolition of the Crow's Nest Pass Freight Rates.

Until a few years ago Bert was one of the largest farmers living in Saskatchewan, taking into account his holdings — about 30 sections — in Colorado. Bert says that he bought land in the States because it was cheaper and he wanted to get away from the "prairie socialists." But Canadians like Bert who swarmed down to Colorado to grow wheat got caught up in an unexpected environmental controversy. The grassland Bert bought and broke caused local residents in Colorado to push for laws to prevent "sodbusting" because of fears that cultivating the light soil would create erosion and, eventually, a dustbowl. In August 1983 Bert sold his Colorado holdings.

BERT: When I started farming in 1959 I began with a half-section of rented land. I worked with my father for four or five years and gradually kept adding land. We've had 17 sections now for about ten years. We sold our land in Colorado because of foreign ownership problems. At one time we farmed up to 47 sections.

I don't know what to think about farming. We used to think it was very good...couldn't beat it...but I don't know as I would coax anybody to start right now. It's pretty disheartening to see so many young people going broke. It's terrible. They put in five or ten of their best years and they just can't do it. The averages are against them.

I don't know what the direction of agriculture is. It's got me beat. I thought I had all the answers a couple of years ago, but not anymore. It's not only the young farmers that are going down, some older ones are going too.

I think the marketing structure is really bad. I'd have to brag about one little thing, which is our greatest claim to fame here. About ten of us started the Palliser Wheat Growers. I was one of the "Original Bad Ten." That was in

the early seventies. At that time Otto Lang was going to make us quit growing wheat. He put the LIFT Program in and the quota based on summerfallow acres. The Palliser Wheat Growers got enough people shook up enough to start asking questions.

I was naive enough to think that all we had to do was go through the country and hold some meetings and pretty soon we'd have everybody with us. We did hit 30,000 members that first couple of months, but they died right back to about 3,000 as soon as they found out that we were against orderly marketing or, as they say in Alberta, orderly non-marketing. The Palliser is still there and it will always be there, but it will never have much weight. There are just not enough people ready for it.

I'm for the open market. It works across the line. Now some of the co-op types and socialists can explain to you why it won't work and it all makes sense if you haven't seen it working somewhere else. You see, this equity business, where everybody is going to be equal, has a bad habit of keeping the non-productive chap going. He can make a living if he wants to stay, but it's not going to be a good living at all and he'd be better off with a job. But this equity business will keep him in business because somehow there's always a government payment of some sort that the bigger farmer has to subsidize the little guy on.

It keeps the system going to where everybody believes that we have to have more than four dollars a bushel for wheat and we have to have cheaper machinery and we have to do this and that just so we can survive. Well, maybe they weren't meant to survive. For instance, I couldn't be a brain surgeon. So if farming is not your thing the quicker you get out of it the better.

I don't think that government controls are the answer, so what else is there? It has to be let the market find its own way. And maybe that's what's happening right now with high interest rates. Maybe it is getting rid of those that shouldn't have been here in the first place.

I know for sure that one man can handle five sections with the machinery available. So a farmer that is just work-

Bert Wildfong,
Craik, Saskatchewan

ing a half or two sections . . . what is he doing with his spare time, really? I don't mind someone making a living if he's working, but maybe some aren't working hard enough. Nobody guaranteed you a good living unless you worked did they? That's the same as working one day a week and expecting to make as much as the guy who works five days.

The way it's going I would bet that there will only be half of us farmers left. You can't put a family on every quarter in this country. You've got to have income and this land is only productive on a large scale. Out here, in this damn little town, when I was a kid, we had a dance every Saturday night and two picture-shows a week. There was two pool-rooms and two bowling alleys and two or three cafés in town. There was something to go to.

Now the kids have to drive to Regina to get a bottle of beer or to go to a show. The culture is dying. It has to. There's not enough people left. People blame us for it. I'm not particularly proud that we farm a lot of land but I don't think it is a lot of land. There are lots of farms in North America ten times bigger than I am.

Immigrants and Hired Hands

Standing in the field it all seemed very normal. Some 500 yards into the broccoli patch eight Mexican farmworkers walked waist-deep in plants, cutting away the vegetables with machetes, chucking them into the tractor-pulled cart, bending again, hacking and chucking. They had been there since seven A.M. and would work 12 hours with two half-hour meal breaks and coffee breaks.

When I arrived in their field the first day, they looked at me curiously and sceptically. They'd seen me riding around with the "boss" and wondered who I was. The second morning, they greeted me with wide smiles. We had become friends the day before. I'd shown them my work and in broken Spanish had tried to tell them why I wanted to photograph them. Our friendship seemed to grow that morning when they saw me walk a half-mile through the wet and muddy broccoli field to join them. I was wet to the hips and they laughed, pointing to their bright yellow waders. They were telling me I could use a pair. I laughed with them and, through sign language and plenty of smiles, I went about my work photographing them at their's.

Mine was the easy job, but they bore no hostility towards me because of it. Miguel, Blás, Olivios, Jésus, Roberto, Séraphine...they had all come from Mexico. For some it was their fifth year working in Canada, for others their first. At $4.50 an hour, twelve hours a day, six days a week, for three to six months of the year, they came to earn Canadian dollars, then return home to feed families of four or five children. Canadian dollars buy much more in Mexico than they do in Canada.

Perhaps the lack of buying power of those same dollars was behind the sober atmosphere in the onion fields. Some 30 farmworkers, primarily Native People, sat on plastic cans or in the dirt. Some knelt while others sat, legs outstretched, in a cleared patch. They worked silently, were friendly but less jovial, and less willing to chat. Depending on the crop, workers are paid either by the hour or by the piece. In the onion patch the standard is 55 cents for a dozen bunches. A fast onion picker might pull ten dozen an hour, cleaned and bound by elastics. If a worker managed to keep up the pace for ten hours, six days a week, he or she might earn $1,300 a month before deductions. But the worker would have to be fast, picking at least two bunches of eight onions every minute.

The day I visited the broccoli and onion patches south of Portage la Prairie, the Manitoba sun offered 33 degrees Celsius and there was no breeze. Shade could be found in the overheated vans or cars that workers had brought to the fields. In the early morning the children, ranging in age from two to thirteen, seemed to be in good spirits. By five o'clock that afternoon one young boy was pulling onions slowly with a grab more intent on mangling than on bunching. He and his younger brothers and three sisters worked the fields, adding their pick to that of their parents. Many teenagers also worked that patch.

Native workers awoke every morning at four-thirty or five o'clock to drive the 60 miles to work from any of the four reserves nearby. Portage la Prairie offers jobs on six large vegetables farms. Often, children come and pool their piecework along with the rest of the family labour. Working together a family makes more money. Besides, with no day care facilities available and a farmworker's wage, babysitters come at a premium.

The day before I'd asked the "boss" — one of the two owners — the age range of the 100 workers who laboured on his 400-acre vegetable farm. "Sixteen to sixty-five," he'd said. In a sense he was right. He doesn't count the children because he doesn't pay them. Instead, the parents are paid for their kids' contribution.

Onion pickers,
Portage la Prairie, Manitoba

158

*Packing broccoli on the assembly line,
Portage la Prairie, Manitoba*

"Who are the best workers?" I ventured.

"The Mexicans. They make good stoop labour. They're not afraid of working hard. They don't drive the equipment or tractors. They're no good at that. But they are great in the fields. I compare them to Canadians who go north to work to get the money. They're only interested in making the money so they work hard, steady, long hours on straight time."

"What are the Indians like?" I asked.

"They mainly work for me so that they can collect UIC in the winter. They're not interested in working hard. I had one Indian here once, he was collecting UIC, plus a wage from me and welfare."

The "boss" didn't make any monetary connection between Mexicans working harder than Indians, if in fact that was the case. A Canadian dollar will buy much more in Mexico than in Canada. While $4.50 an hour may seem like a gift from heaven to Mexican farmworkers, for Canadians it is cheap labour. As cheap as what the Mexicans work for in their own country.

These farmowners grow mainly root crops and turn over $1.3 million in an average year. They spray about $50,000 worth of chemicals on 400 acres. While input costs are high on any farm, each owner clears a salary of about $20,000 a year. But the "boss" quickly adds that business trips, vehicles, insurance, and even his home are company benefits. Still, the boss was adamant. "There's a lot of pressure in farming. A farmworkers' union is the last thing we want."

A strong union might have been able to deal with the problem that existed in the onion patch the day I was visiting. An adjacent field, only 100 yards away, had been sprayed. The drift, although light, had headed towards the patch of farmworkers. Two of the women were pregnant and had no idea of what was being sprayed or the potential effects.

Still, the vegetable farms south of Portage la Prairie are said to be among the best on the prairies. One of the reasons is that, unlike other provinces, farmworkers in Manitoba have an association that tries to negotiate standardized wages and working conditions as well as provide a stable workforce. But the association has to depend on verbal agreements. It is not a union and consequently has no legal recourse if a grower decides not to follow "the guidelines."

Manitoba farmworkers began to organize in 1976. At first a union was thought to be the answer, but it was too difficult to organize and met with strong opposition from the growers. So farmworkers settled for the formation of the Manitoba Farmworkers Association, now with about 350 members. About 90 per cent of the members, who pay a token fee of $1 a year, are Native People. Women make up 60 per cent of all members. The association has made inroads with salaries, getting water and toilets into the fields and improving worker housing so that at least hot and cold running water is available. As well, field supervisors are often Native. But even the organizers of the association agree that while they are ahead of most contract farmworkers on the prairies, there is a long way to go.

There are approximatley 39,000 farmworkers in the

western prairie provinces. A portion of that figure, one that is hard to estimate, roam to vegetable farms as migrant workers. The average hourly rate, one suggested by the federal farm-labour pool, is about $4.75 an hour. Some contract workers are paid by the piece. In 1983 Alberta beet workers were paid $20 an acre for the first hoeing and $8 an acre for the second and third. Thinning out crowded plants garnered $30 an acre. An average worker might complete an acre of thinning in a day. Housing, working conditions, and pay rates, however, vary from region to region. Some Alberta workers have nicknamed their temporary homes "lizard house" or "snakehouse" after the reptiles that have permanent residency there.

On the majority of prairie farms, workers are the traditional "hired hands." They often work alongside farmowners seeding and harvesting. They receive the best pay and working conditions, on average earning $6 to $8 an hour or $1,000 a month with room and board.

Offshore or immigrant workers make up a small percentage of the total farmworker force. In 1981, about 5,000 Mexicans and Caribbean workers were brought into Canada, most of them working on factory farms in the east.

While the situation of farmworkers varies across the prairies, these workers share a number of things in common. For one, their wages have always lagged behind those of urban industrial workers. In addition, they are excluded from provincial labour codes. Minimum wage rates, child-labour laws, overtime, holiday pay, hours of work, and job security provisions do not apply to farmworkers. While the workers pay into the Canada Pension Plan and Unemployment Insurance, workers' compensation is at the discretion of the employer, and occupational health and safety legislation is rarely enforced. Only three provinces in Canada have mandatory workers' compensation for farmworkers, although farming is the third most hazardous industry in North America. Most other occupations came under the legislation around 1915.

Farmworkers perform back-breaking work, yet are the least protected employees in our society. On the prairies no farmworker belongs to a union. Attempts were made in the 1930s to organize beet workers in Alberta, but those efforts failed due to heavy opposition from growers and processors. Organizing agricultural workers on the prairies is difficult because the workforce is transient and often isolated. More often than not farmworkers are unskilled, uneducated, or for one reason or another excluded from the standard workforce. They are Native People, women, children, the aged, prisoners, or unemployed youth. And in some cases they are former farmowners.

While most farmers have historically been opposed to unionization of farmworkers there is a definite connection between the loss of the family farm and the abuse of farmworkers. While family farms have been on the decrease the number of farmworkers has increased. In Saskatchewan 60 per cent of full-time farmworkers are employed on the 1 per cent of farms that have more than one paid worker. As farm operations have become fewer and larger the number of farmworkers has increased.

And while many family farmers see the protection of farmworkers as an infringement on their individual operations, the forces squeezing both groups are much the same. The abuse of farmworkers and the loss of the family farm have the same root cause. Land concentration and a policy of providing cheap food victimize both and ignore the human costs.

RICHARD CHASKE was one of the organizers of the Manitoba Farmworkers Association in 1976 and for a time was its president. Prior to that Richard spent 13 years as a farmworker on the vegetable farms near Portage la Prairie.

RICHARD: A union is hard to organize but would give us more legal status and leverage. When we were organizing, everybody thought it was going to be a union so they followed us every which way we went. They chased us off the fields. They stopped us from coming down the field roads. They threatened to fire people. They tried to give us shit jobs so we'd quit. It took three years to form this association. Today we have a very good working relationship with most of the growers.

Before our association was formed housing was very bad. We found people in barns and in chicken coops, granaries and run-down cabooses. There were also problems with wages. Some employers would promise so many dollars per acre, then when the job was finished the workers received lower dollars than what they had agreed on. We have wages and working conditions that are better now and there is a housing program that is run by the provincial and federal governments.

The wages vary from farm to farm. When I worked on the farm I was getting 50 cents an hour. At that time minimum wage was a dollar and 25 cents. Now the workers are getting 50 cents above minimum wage. I don't think the wages are high enough, but then it used to be a lot worse. It should be set at six dollars an hour today.

Right now we're looking into farm labour legislation, which is a big thing. We want recognition as labourers, as farmworkers. We aren't even recognized by any labour law in the province. The Employment Standards Act, which includes hours of work, wages, etc., doesn't apply. We may be getting all of those things right now, but it is only a gentleman's agreement with the growers. We pay all the deductions like income tax, unemployment insurance, pension plan, so we should be recognized the same as any other worker.

I used to say that farmworkers are just like their ma-chines, you know. They turn us on in the morning and shut us off in the evening. That's the way I felt about the whole thing, but things are getting better. As long as we can maintain our gentleman's agreement that's the only lever we have.

Our workers have very limited education. Many of them are scared to speak up and ask whether a chemical is safe or what precautions they should be taking. If we have a problem — say the job is unsafe and we don't want to work — we can't refuse to work. Basically all we can do is talk to the employer.

On one farm the packing workers were getting gased with carbon monoxide fumes. The employer would run to town to get a bottle of aspirins and give them all two or three each. We called the health inspector and he shut that shop down for repair.

The children out in the fields are a big concern. Because it's only a seasonal job the adult workers try to bring in their kids to make as much money as fast as possible. I don't think that a kid under 12 should be in the fields, because kids will go and grab a carrot that has just been sprayed with chemical and eat it or run to another field when their parents aren't watching. You know, things like that are unsafe.

There are quite a few Mexicans working out here too. I feel that immigrant workers should belong to our organization. We don't care about white, black, or brown, we look at ourselves as all brothers and sisters. This year we spoke on their behalf and asked that they be treated the same. They need to be recognized as well.

For instance, they have their own set of traditional holidays that they like to celebrate. The owners used to make them work hours on end. We felt that was wrong. They should be asked if they want to work those hours. They should be recognized as farmworkers and not just people who don't know the language and are just brought here and put in the fields to work and when it gets dark you bring 'em in and put them back out again as soon as the daylight comes around. It's getting a bit better now because of the association, but there's a ways to go.

It's very hard for the Mexicans because they can't communicate. If they have a problem they can't explain it to the employer. We had an incident last year with a Mexican. He wanted to go home because he had received a letter that one of his immediate family was dying, and I couldn't communicate with him. He eventually did go home a week later. But there again it's just like putting a person on a blacklist...once you leave the job... that's it...you've broken the contract and they don't want you back here anymore. They'll replace him with somebody else.

"Off-shore" workers,
Portage la Prairie, Manitoba

KILBURN ANNETS — Kibby, as he's called by his friends — has spent most of his life on the farm. During the 1970s he worked in the British Columbia sawmills for seven years before returning to the land as a farm labourer for Arrison Farms Ltd., near Bassano, Alta. He admits that he would like to farm on his own, but the economics prevent him from buying back in. In his quiet reserved manner he tells me that working on a farm is the next best thing to being a farmowner.

KILBURN: I farmed for ten years up in the Peace Country of Alberta. But I quit in 1969 when I was 40. There was too damn much rain and snow. I owned seven quarters, but I lost two crops in a row because of the rain and I could see the financial problems coming so I sold out. It was too expensive to start up again somewhere else. It was just at the time when land values were beginning to rise.

Farming is my trade. I class it as a trade anyways. Working in the sawmills was okay for awhile. Working in industry you have benefits that you don't have on the farm, like dental plans, pension plans, workers' compensation, and group insurance. But I don't think the farmer can afford those benefits.

I like working on the farm. I wish I was farming for myself but there's no way. It would take almost a million dollars to get started.

I think in 50 years either the Hutterites or big corporations will own most of the land. That's the way it seems to be going anyway.

Kilburn "Kibby" Annets,
Bassano, Alberta

FRANK BRYSKI seems unusually relaxed as he drives a large computerized combine on land near Yorkton, Sask. Although it's harvest time and most farmers are rushed and their minds are geared towards dealing with mishaps and slowdowns, Frank seems to have no worries. At 49 Frank has turned from a farmer into a farm labourer and the transition seems to fit him well. He sold his quarter a few years ago and now works for Lutz Enterprises Ltd.

FRANK: I like to come out here and work as a farm labourer. I miss the harvest. You get psyched up for it.

In 1980 I thought it was time to get out of farming on my own. It was getting too costly with the machinery. It was no use continuing. I'll always work on the farm, but now I'm my own boss. I have no stress, no headaches, and I can pretty well work my own hours. I don't have to worry if the machinery breaks down. It's not my problem.

I started farming in 1959 and I did custom work. I used to go spraying for two-bits an acre. I liked it but it seemed that in order to make it you had to keep getting larger. I'll tell you the reason I never went bigger as a farmer . . . it's a juggling act. You buy another section so you're doing more acres. So you wear out the machinery. So you buy more machinery. So then you have to buy more land to pay for the new machinery to make it work more hours for you.

Right now I earn eight dollars an hour. You're not making any money as a farm labourer. You can't live on part-time work and 5,000 dollars a year — no way.

I think farming is all politics. It's a big game and a big gamble. You have to ask yourself: "Who are you working for?" That's the real question.

Frank Bryski,
Yorkton, Saskatchewan

JACIE SKELTON   In the early 1970s Jacie Skelton returned to the farming community near Sinclair, Man., where she had grown up. Jacie is 32, a single mother, a farm labourer on her family's farm, and actively involved in the National Farmers Union as a regional co-ordinator.

As a farm labourer Jacie's main concern stems from the question: "Who controls the land?" She doesn't believe that farmers do. She knows that farm labourers don't. She says that farmers are forced to produce food as cheaply as possible to meet production costs, and therein lies the control. Jacie says that everyone has to understand that cheap food controls what is done with the land and what is being done to the farmer. Today's family farm and the opportunity for future generations of farmers are slipping away.

JACIE: I love the land. I like the peacefulness of the country-side. That's what keeps me here. I have connections to the farm I was brought up on and I always want to be part of that. I see the importance of producing food and I want to be linked to that.

As far as economics go there's no logical reason to produce food. It's just something in me. I see the food producer as the most important person in the world. I find that exciting and challenging. It's challenging to work the land and the machinery and see things grow and harvested. The really fabulous time is harvest. That's when you see the fruits of your effort.

The main frustration is the amount of mechanization that we deal with daily — the size of equipment we use to cover the amount of land we need to make a living. I'm constantly thinking about how we could produce food with less mechanization and have more people involved — more people catching the bug and loving the land. I feel frustration when I look at the Canadian trends — more mechanization, constantly being told to produce more grain for export — when in fact maybe we should be looking more at our domestic needs and producing what's good for the land and good for people.

I don't own any land. Why can't I own land? Why don't I?

I keep wondering how we can develop policies so that young people who want to farm can. Sometimes I feel like a foreigner to the land because I know how easy it would be for me to lose the opportunity to farm.

If you don't control the land base you have no security. Although I am a farm labourer on my family's farm and I know in time I will become part-owner of this land, I know there are things that could change that … things that could wipe out my chances. The production of food, the way it is produced and the quality all depend on who controls the land.

I look at young people who would likely choose farming as a career if they could afford to — but they definitely can't so they go other ways. I think that's a real loss to Canada.

In my eyes family food production is important because it's a way of life. The land is concentrating now, which means more farm labourers who have no control over the land — over how it's farmed or how it's mined and they don't have any control over what's produced.

What we see happening is a lot of seasonal workers on low wages or you see labourers under terrific strain because farmers don't understand why labourers don't want to work as hard as they do. They haven't twigged to the fact that it's because as labourers they have no direct interest or participation on the land. And so you have a lot of farm-labour problems.

Still, you have to reach a certain size before you can hire farm labour. Other than that family labour is used. Some farmers now are having a heck of a hard time surviving. They see themselves losing ground every day. They say to themselves that if there are no rewards after 25 or 40 years then they don't want to see their children farm. They want them to go to the city and have security, time off, holidays, and time to enjoy themselves.

I see that trend as very dangerous because the only way to move into farming is through a family operation. So then, what happens? Within two generations we won't have very many farms being turned over. So who's going to be farming and where will all the kids go?

When I came home to farm we had to go through a lot of

over through inheritance, and because mom won't be getting any monetary return in her old age we'll have to ensure that she has the things she needs and wants to live with. Until parents and children can see that sort of thing and trust each other... then we will still be caught in the situation of "Well, then I'd better sell." A responsibility is created not only of the parent to the child but the child to the parent, and that creates a bond and a link in life.

We need to stop the escalating price of land. Why is there speculative price on a natural resource that's necessary for the production of food? Maybe there should be no price. Maybe land should be held in trust for the future generations to produce food. Right now, it's being mined so people can pay the speculative price.

In our community there are two values on land. The one is the value that the ordinary farmers can pay, the other is the higher value that foreigners are willing to pay. So, if you're lucky, a farmer may offer you the land at 50,000 dollars a quarter while foreigners are willing to pay 70,000 to 85,000 dollars a quarter for the same land.

I can't afford either. And the land, if you take into account commodity prices and input costs, is really only worth 25,000 dollars a quarter, if that much. The price of land has no relationship to its productive value.

I want to farm my family's land because of the life I lived on that land, because of the relationship I saw my father having with that land. He loved the land, he loved the work and animals. He always respected what was living and that includes the land. If we're not careful the cultural practices we use will kill the life and fibre of the land. We have to address that quickly before our land doesn't produce anymore.

Jacie Skelton and Margaret Hayward,
Sinclair, Manitoba

discussion before my mother could understand that I really wanted to farm and farm the land that I had grown up on. Now it's no problem, but before that... until that understanding was there... it was some battle because you have parents sitting in the position of needing money for retirement — of wanting to finally be able to relax — and you have young people who can't afford to be saddled with the burden that is required to turn the farm over. So, in order to find a way that young people can take over and the older people can afford to live in dignity for the rest of their lives, it takes a lot of openness and innovation.

What we're looking at on our farm is turning the land

Notes for City Slickers

BEEFFALO: the name of the meat produced from an animal which is the progeny of cross-breeding between the buffalo and a bovine animal.

CANADIAN WHEAT BOARD: Canada's international marketing agency for grain. It has been the exclusive marketer of grain — wheat, oats, barley — for more than 40 years. The Board had the exclusive right to handle the domestic marketing of feed grains until 1974, when that right was taken away. Oilseeds are handled by the private trade.

FARM CREDIT CORPORATION: a federal agency that provides agricultural loans to farmers. It was formed in 1959 under legislation that revamped its predecessor, the Canadian Farm Loan Board, founded in 1929.

FARMSTART: a provincial government program in Saskatchewan, which lends farmers start-up funds. All western provincial governments have similar programs.

HARVESTORES: large, tall, cylindrical storage bins.

LIFT PROGRAM: the acronym for "Lower Inventories for Tomorrow," a highly controversial program of 1970 that paid farmers not to grow wheat. It was initiated by Otto Lang, a former transport minister responsible for the Canadian Wheat Board.

PÉPIN PLAN: refers to the program that Jean-Luc Pépin, the former federal transport minister, initiated to change the Statutory Crow's Nest Pass Freight Rate Agreement.

QUARTER: a quarter of a section, or 160 acres.

QUONSET: a large, arched, wooden or metal barn.

RAILGRADE BEEF: beef carcasses that have been graded and readied for shipment.

SECTION: 640 acres

SUMMERFALLOW: when the land is seeded on alternating years.

VOLUNTEER GRAIN: unwanted seeds that germinate in a field, usually seed left over from a previous year.

WHITE CROW CAMPAIGN: a protest organized by prairie farmers to oppose changes to the Crow's Nest Pass Freight Rate Agreement. The farmers rode by rail to Ottawa and presented several large wooden crows, signed in black by farmers, to the House of Commons in March 1982.

ZERO-TILL: also referred to as "no-till," a method of seeding that eliminates the cultivation of soil and often the use of summerfallow.

Pro-Crow demonstrators,
Regina, Saskatchewan

COLOPHON

The text of *Prairie Lives* was typeset in Rector and Alphagothic; the cover and title pages were set in Baskerville.

Designed by Public Good.

Typesetting and pagination by Canadian Composition. Printed by Arthurs-Jones Lithographing Ltd. on Warren Patina Matte and Lustro Dull Cover.

Published by Between The Lines, 1985.